1001
WRISTWATCHES

HISTORY • TECHNOLOGY • DESIGN

This is a Parragon Publishing Book
This edition published by Parragon in 2010
Copyright © Parragon Books Ltd 2010

Parragon Publishing
Queen Street House
4 Queen Street
Bath BA1 1HE, UK

Copyright © 2006 Heel Verlag GmbH, Königswinter
HEEL Verlag GmbH
Gut Pottscheidt
53639 Königswinter
Email: info@heel-verlag.de

Written by Martin Häussermann
Additional text by Peter Braun, Gerhard Claussen
Photographs from the archives of the author and manufacturers
Layout: Grafikbüro Schumacher, Königswinter
Lithography: Colibri, Petra Hammermann, Königswinter

US edition produced by Cambridge Publishing Management Ltd
Translation: Susan James & Theresa Pike
Editing: Juliet Mozley
Proofreading: Alison Rasch

ISBN 978-1-4454-2703-4

Printed in Indonesia

1001
WRISTWATCHES

HISTORY • TECHNOLOGY • DESIGN

EDITOR: MARTIN HÄUSSERMANN

Bath · New York · Singapore · Hong Kong · Cologne · Delhi
Melbourne · Amsterdam · Johannesburg · Auckland · Shenzhen

CONTENTS

Dear Reader,

To be honest, the mechanical watch is really an anachronism, because a battery-operated quartz watch costing 25 dollars is certainly at least as accurate a timepiece. Apart from that there are time displays on cell phones, organizers, cars, and in airplane cockpits. But the fact remains: We wouldn't like to be without our mechanical watches—even in these modern times, or maybe even as an antidote to the digital overkill that poses a daily threat in the workplace and in our everyday life. The mechanical watch invites us to view it not just as a tool, but as a work of art, and to pause a little while we do so. It is an expression of personal style, a reliable traveling companion, and thanks to automatic or hand winding, it still tells us the time when the batteries in a quartz watch or cell phone are fading fast. And that's something they have a tendency to do without warning and at the most inconvenient time.

Another point: At a time when sustainability is the buzzword everywhere you go, what better example can there be than the mechanical watch? It is an investment for life—and even beyond. While batteries and—sooner or later—the whole quartz watch will end up on the garbage heap, mechanical watches will, sooner or later, simply be passed on. Forgetting all the factual arguments that men in particular make in order to justify unnecessary purchases such as fast cars, amazing airplanes or even expensive watches, we would just like to say: All these things are just tremendous fun.

At the same time, we're always spoiled for choice, even where watches are concerned. Those of us who are more practically minded choose an automatic watch with an easily read display which might show the date as well as the time. Those of a more frivolous nature aspire to a chronograph with a stopwatch function that isn't just handy for timing sporting events, but also comes into its own when grilling a steak or boiling an egg. Divers buy special diving watches; pilots and would-be pilots are more likely to favor an aviator watch. Finally, globetrotters opt for a watch that displays different time zones.

This book is a compendium of all sorts of watches arranged according to their purpose and function—with over 1,000 photographs of watches documenting almost 100 years of timepiece history. It also contains information about the various types of watches and their backgrounds. By the time you've read it, you won't just know the history of the Tourbillon, but will also be able to tell the difference between a chronograph and a chronometer.

Apropos chronometers, a mechanical watch really is pretty accurate. Good watches, which have been individually adjusted for the wearer, go fast or slow by a maximum of five seconds a day. This equates to an accuracy of 99.9998 percent.

The editor would sincerely like to thank the authors and photographers who have not just contributed to the success of this book, but who through their regular contributions to the *Armbanduhren* ("Wristwatches") magazine have demonstrated that their technical knowledge of watches is indeed moving with the times.

Martin Häussermann

1. MEN'S WATCHES

The clock is the oldest independently working mechanical device that we know. The possibility of being able to measure something as vague as time is part of its fascination. This is enhanced by the fact that the mechanical clock is one of the most accurate machines that there is. On the following pages, which are illustrated with the finest men's watches from the past nine decades, we would like to introduce you to the function of a mechanical watch.

Audemars Piguet
Chronometer, yellow gold, manually
wound, caliber VZSS, from 1951

Seen from a purely practical point of view, a watch is a dispensable object. We are surrounded by clocks wherever we go. We see them on computer screens, cell phones, the car and in all public places. However, men in particular like to wear watches, partly because a watch is a man's only legitimate piece of jewelry, partly because they are fascinated by the technology that keeps this micromechanical masterpiece going. On the following pages you will discover how the tiny little mechanism inside these fine timekeepers works.

Roughly speaking, the movement can be divided into the mainspring, gear train, escapement and regulating system. This arrangement does, however, exclude two vital assemblies, namely the motion work which is required to transform the continuing motion of a movement with

Audemars Piguet
Ultra-thin, platinum, manually
wound, AP caliber 2003, from 1999

Audemars Piguet
Men's watch for Cartier, yellow gold,
manually wound, caliber 2001LEC,
from 1955

Audemars Piguet
Jump Hour, white gold, manually
wound, from 1925

hands and dial into a practical visual display, and the winding mechanism.

Winding

"When I wind up my watch should I turn the little wheel in both directions or just in one?" This is a question frequently asked of watchmakers by people who wear a mechanical watch with a manual winding mechanism. It is generally too complicated to explain the technicalities, so he or she might simply reply that when you wind a watch it doesn't matter whether you turn the "little wheel" (the crown) backwards and forwards between your thumb and index finger, or rotate it forward, reposition your fingers, then rotate forward again. It really doesn't matter, because a watch can only be wound up in one direction, generally by turning the crown clockwise

Audemars Piguet
Automatic, white gold, automatic, caliber K2072, from 1965

Audemars Piguet
Millenary Automatic, yellow gold, automatic, AP caliber 2125, from 1999

Audemars Piguet
Men's watch with digital display, white gold, manually wound, caliber GHSM, from 1929

Audemars Piguet
Jules Audemars 3120 "Globe," red gold, automatic, AP caliber 3120, from 2006

Audemars Piguet
Royal Oak "Jumbo," steel, automatic, AP caliber 2121, from 2006

Audemars Piguet
Edward Piguet Automatic, red gold, automatic, AP caliber 2121, from 2006

Officine Panerai hand-wind movement with eight-day power reserve

Baume & Mercier
Hampton, steel, automatic, Baume & Mercier caliber BM 13750 (base caliber ETA 2000), from 1999

(if you are looking straight at the center of the crown).

If you turn the crown counterclockwise, you barely feel any resistance, because this is a neutral gear mode. What happens is that the winding pinion and clutch wheel, both of which have identical interlocking ramped teeth, disengage and slide along past each other. This takes us neatly on to the gearing mechanism.

The link between the movement and the outside world is via a thin steel shaft with a long pin at one end, with which it is mounted into a recess in the base plate of the watch. On the other end, which protrudes from the watch, it has a male thread on to which the winding crown is screwed. The term "winding stem," generally used for the shaft described

here, is actually an inadequate description because it is also used for setting the time, i.e. moving the hands. On modern wristwatches this shaft also serves a third function in addition to those of winding and setting the time: It is also used for quick adjustment of the date.

The power source

The power source of a clockwork movement has remained essentially unchanged for hundreds of years: a long, flat metal spring, coiled up and fixed at both ends. The resulting opposing forces provide the driving power for the watch. When the first pocket watches were invented, the time came to say goodbye to the perfect power source for a clockwork movement: the pendulum. The advantages of the portable clock were somewhat counteracted by the

Blancpain
Villeret ultra-slim, steel, automatic,
Blancpain caliber 1153, from 2006

Baume & Mercier
Classima, yellow gold, automatic,
Baume & Mercier caliber BM
18922 (base caliber ETA 2892-
A2), from 1999

Baume & Mercier
Hampton Classic, yellow gold, quartz,
ETA 901.001, from 2006

Blancpain
Ultra-slim watch, yellow gold,
automatic, Blancpain caliber
1735, from 1999

Blu
Terzett, rose gold, automatic, caliber
blu-Orbit (base caliber ETA 2892-A2),
from 2006

Baume & Mercier
Classima Executives XL, steel, manually wound,
BM caliber 16498 (base caliber ETA 6498-2), from 2006

23

Rainer Brand
Panama, steel, automatic, ETA caliber
2892-A2, from 1999

Breguet
Manually wound, yellow gold, Breguet
caliber 530, from 1999

Martin Braun
Bigdate, steel, automatic,
TT caliber 651 (base caliber
ETA 2892-A2), from 2006

distinct disadvantage of an irregular power source. A grandfather clock or wall clock with a pendulum is driven by a steady, constant torque. A clock's accuracy is dependent solely upon making adjustments to the gear train, escapement and regulating system (balance/pendulum). Not so, however, with a spring-powered watch. In this case one of the possible causes for timekeeping errors lies in the uncoiling action of the mainspring, as the power curve is non-linear.

The spring

The mainspring provides the energy that drives the watch. A spring-powered movement is the only mechanism that requires just one burst of energy to provide its services for up to 45 hours (and in the case of modern automatic watches, for far in excess of 50 hours) without the addition of fuel, air pressure or steam. A turbine cannot function without a continuous supply of steam, nor can a car engine run without fuel burning constantly, and the modern household collapses if deprived of electricity. The quartz watch and the car

Bunz
Moontime, steel/yellow gold,
automatic, ETA caliber 2892-2,
from 1999

Bulova
Limited Edition, yellow gold,
automatic ETA caliber 1120,
from 1999

Breguet
Tonneau, yellow gold,
automatic, Breguet caliber
532, from 1999

Breguet
Classic ultra-slim, yellow gold,
automatic, Breguet caliber 502.3,
from 2006

Bulgari
Bulgari, platinum, automatic, Bulgari
caliber BU220 (base caliber Girard-
Perregaux 220), from 2006

Bulgari
Bulgari Moon Phases, white gold, automatic, LIP caliber 3103 (base caliber ETA 2892-A2), from 2006

Cartier
Square, yellow gold, manually wound, from 1970

Cartier
Santos Dumont, manually wound, caliber 21, from 1980

Cartier
Crash watch, yellow gold, manually wound, from 1991

have one thing in common: If the tank (coin cell) is empty, the only thing they are both still capable of doing is showing us the extent to which we depend upon them. The question as to whether a mainspring is, figuratively speaking, a fuel or an engine isn't that easy to answer—it's both.

The mainspring isn't like a rubber band, which can be stretched, but when released relaxes and finally hangs slack. Even the spring of a watch that has run down still has a considerable residual tension and would continue to uncoil quite a lot if there was sufficient room within the watch. Mainsprings are literally as hard as steel, have a very dense molecular structure and are accordingly brittle. In days gone by, when springs made from cold rolled steel were used, the task of replacing a mainspring that had

suddenly snapped for no particular reason was a regular job for any watchmaker.

"I've overwound my watch," confesses the guilty customer to the watchmaker. But just to clear up a widespread misunderstanding: even the owner of a delicate ladies' watch would have to take a pair of pliers to her little watch to "overwind" the mainspring. This holds true today more than ever, because in normal use the springs used in modern watches are unbreakable. As usual, the exception proves the rule. The replacement mainsprings used so frequently by watchmakers in the past were either simple flat-rolled steel bands that had acquired their material springiness through hardening and tempering, or their residual stress by cold rolling. These springs had a hole at each end. One hole was used to attach one

Cartier
Reverso, yellow gold, manually wound, caliber 838/1, from 1980

Cartier
Santos 100, red gold, automatic, Cartier caliber 49 (base caliber ETA 2892), from 2006

Cartier
Roadster XL, steel, automatic, Cartier caliber 8500 (base caliber ETA 2893), from 2006

Cartier
Pasha de Cartier, white gold, automatic, Cartier caliber 115, 24-hour display, from 1999

end of the spring to the hook on what is known as the barrel arbor. The other end was secured to the hook of the barrel within which the spring was now coiled.

When the winding stem of the watch is turned and this turning action is transferred to the ratchet wheel via the clutch wheel, winding pinion, and crown wheel, the transfer of power to the movement also begins. At this moment the mainspring, which up until now had been wound hard up against the wall of the barrel, and which is attached by its hole to a hook on the barrel arbor, is drawn to the center of the barrel. With every turn of the winding crown, the mainspring winds itself tighter around the barrel arbor. At the same time it tries to pull the barrel itself along with it, in an attempt to uncoil itself again as far as possible. Consequently, the barrel begins to turn, and its toothed rim transmits the driving force to the watch's gear train.

The driving force

Modern springs

The development of the springs used nowadays goes back to the Swiss engineer Max Straumann. In the early 1950s Straumann introduced a significant new development in the area of watch springs under the name of "Nivaflex." In numerous experiments Straumann had made up an alloy from iron, nickel, chrome, cobalt, beryllium and other additives. Springs manufactured from this material are rust-resistant, unbreakable, cannot be magnetized, and are fatigue-proof. A Nivaflex spring can be wound up 10,000 times without losing its strength, so if wound up daily, it will give more than 27 years' reliable service. The springs used today are coated with a special lubricating layer, which means that they don't require further lubrication by a watchmaker and ensures reduced friction between the individual layers of the spring.

Chopard
Tonneau Power Reserve, yellow gold, automatic, Frédéric Piguet caliber 9644, power reserve indicator, from 1999

Chopard
L.U.C. 1.96, yellow gold, automatic, L.U.C. caliber 1.96, C.O.S.C. certified chronometer, from 2006

Chronoswiss
Régulateur Réctangulaire, yellow gold, manually wound, caliber FHF 29 (introduced 1934), from 1993

Chopard
St. Moritz, steel, automatic, Jaeger-LeCoultre caliber 889, from 1999

Chopard
L.U.C. Quattro, platinum, manually wound, L.U.C. caliber 1.98, C.O.S.C. certified chronometer, from 2006

Chronoswiss
Régulateur, steel, automatic, Chronoswiss caliber C.122 (base caliber Enicar 165), from 1999

Chronoswiss
Kairos, steel, automatic, base caliber
ETA 2892-2, from 1999

Chronoswiss
Digiteur, red gold, automatic,
FEF caliber 130, from 2006

The gear train

In a mechanical watch, the parts of the gear train are akin to an industrial laborer whose performance within the system as a whole is rarely mentioned, but who is nevertheless an important and indispensable member of the team. It is rare for the "workers" in the "gear train department" of a watch to put in an official appearance. The balance and anchor, the hands and dial are always in the limelight. But who knows what a third wheel or fourth wheel pinion is? These unsung workers, who make sure that the power from the mainspring arrives, much changed, at the regulating system, deserve a special mention. "It's running like clockwork," is a phrase we sometimes say when we want to emphasize that something is going particularly well. A precision-made and perfectly functioning gear train is a prerequisite

Chronoswiss
Orea, steel, manually wound,
Chronoswiss caliber C.111, from 1999

Chronoswiss
Régulateur, yellow gold, automatic,
Chronoswiss caliber C.122 (base
caliber Enicar 165), from 2006

for accurate timekeeping. For watchmakers, the "train" is always primarily the toothed gearing that starts at the gear rim of the barrel and ends at the escapement wheel pinion.

Two operating systems

Enigmatic workers with unusual names

To the layman, the names of the wheels appear somewhat confusing. For instance, the minute wheel doesn't carry the minute hand, nor does it make one revolution in one minute. It is the second wheel that carries the cannon pinion, which bears the minute hand, and it makes one revolution in one hour. And it is the fourth wheel, which carries the second hand on its extended pinion, that makes one revolution in one minute.

If we take the minute and fourth wheels as an example, it is clear that the watch designer doesn't have a great deal of room for maneuver when designing a watch movement. He has to configure it in such a way that the minute wheel and its pinion go round once in one hour, while the fourth wheel must make 60 revolutions within that same timespan. The speed with which the other wheels of the movement turn, the number of teeth on the wheels and pinions, the length and strength of the mainspring, or the number of vibrations per hour of the balance—all of these issues are irrelevant for a watch's time display as long as the gear ratios are configured in such a way that the minute wheel and fourth wheel make the requisite number of revolutions.

Corum
Admiral's Cup, steel, quartz driven, ETA caliber 256.111, from 1999

Corum
Golden Bridge, yellow gold, manually wound, Corum caliber Golden Bridge, from 1999

Cimier
C1951 Automatic, steel, automatic, ETA caliber 2836-2, from 2006

Frédérique Constant
Classic Heartbeat Manufacture Moon, steel, manually wound, Frédérique Constant caliber FC 915, with moon phase display, from 2006

Elegant men's watches in gold-plated steel casing from Edox, Cimier, and Davosa.

33

Corum
US$20 Coin Watch, yellow gold, automatic, Corum caliber CO 082 (base caliber ETA 2892-A2), from 2006

Cuervo y Sobrinos
Prominente S.T., steel, automatic, ETA caliber 2671, from 2006

Cyclos
a.m./p.m., steel, automatic, Cyclos caliber CW 1 (base caliber ETA 2992-A2), C.O.S.C. certified chronometer, extending and retracting hour hand, from 2006

Corum
Bubble Skeleton, steel, automatic, ETA caliber 2892-A2, full skeleton dial, from 2006

The hour wheel, which carries the hour hand (known to many as the "little" hand), makes its revolution once every 12 hours. However, the hour wheel belongs not to the gear train, but to the motion works. These design features only become important when the watchmaker is considering the length of time a watch is required to run after a single winding, or the type of escapement or regulating system that is going to be used. Because of course a minute wheel goes around approximately only once every hour. The selection and interaction of the other parts of the movement are crucial in the watchmaker's quest to achieve perfection, whereby the minute wheel must make one revolution in exactly one hour, and by the end of that hour the second hand must have made its tiny jerky movements around the dial exactly 60 times. A fully wound wristwatch would unwind in less than a minute if it were not

Davosa
Classic, steel, manually wound, ETA caliber 2804, from 2006

De Grisogono

Instrumento No.Uno, steel, automatic,
ETA 2892-A2 with module for dual time
zone display, from 2006

Du Bois & Fils

Montre Classique, yellow gold,
automatic, ETA caliber 2892-A2,
from 2006

Delma

Le Brassus, steel, automatic,
ETA caliber 2892-A2, from 1999

Dubey & Schaldenbrand

Aerodyn Chronometer, steel,
automatic, ETA caliber 2892-A2 with
24-hour display, from 1999

Delma

Klondike 1998, yellow gold, automatic,
ETA caliber 2892-A2, power reserve
indicator and 24-hour display, from 1999

35

Dubey & Schaldenbrand
Aerodyn Trophée, rose gold, Aurore caliber 19, from 2006

Ebel
1911, steel, quartz driven, Ebel caliber 187, from 1999

Eberhard
Aqua 8, steel, manually wound, base caliber ETA 7001 Peseux with module for eight-day power reserve, from 1999

Enigma
Bezel Manual Winder, steel, manually wound, ETA caliber Peseux 7001, power reserve display, winding and adjustment of hands by rotating bezel, from 1999

Louis Erard
Longue Ligne Power Reserve, steel, manually wound, ETA caliber Peseux 7001, power reserve display, from 1999

Louis Erard
Heritage Cadran Paris, steel, automatic,
ETA caliber 2824-2, from 2006

Eterna
1935, steel, automatic, ETA caliber
2681, from 1999

Eterna
KonTiki 20, steel, automatic, Eterna
caliber 1489K, from 1968

Eberhard
Les Grandes Courbées, steel, automatic,
Eberhard caliber 3513 (base caliber
ETA 2892-A2), power reserve display, from 2006

stopped in its tracks by the escapement and
balance wheel. The only visible sign of its work
is the jerky way in which the second hand
makes its revolutions.

The imperfect drive

Each gear drive is basically a testament to the
theoretical possibilities of what can be achieved
in practice. One might think that two circular
discs which glide smoothly over each other
would form the ideal basis for a perfect gear
train. Unfortunately, however, the theory of the
perfect gear train does not take into account the
practical issues, for example, wear and tear of
the surfaces interacting with each other,
slippage (i.e. the sliding of the discs upon one
another), improper storage, imbalances, and a
whole variety of other factors.

Eterna
Porsche Design P 10, steel,
automatic, Eterna Matic caliber 633
(base caliber ETA 2824-2), from 1999

Eterna
1948 Grand Date, steel, automatic,
Eterna caliber 608 (base caliber
ETA 2892-A2) from 2006

Fabergé
Agathon, white gold, automatic,
ETA caliber 2892-A2, from 2006

Gérald Genta
Retro Les Fantasies, steel, automatic,
Gérald Genta caliber GA3 (base caliber
ETA 2892-A2), from 1999

Jacques Etoile
Lune & Etoile, steel, automatic,
ETA caliber 2824-2 with moon
phase display, from 2006

It was for this reason that mechanical engineers and watch designers both chose the second best, but more practically realistic option: a toothed system. While mechanical engineering generally employs gear wheels whose triangular teeth have had their points flattened, watch manufacturers use something known as a (psendo) cycloid gear mechanism.

In this kind of tooth system the sides of the teeth have a curved, almost half-rounded profile, enabling them to "roll off" each other easily. This reduces the energy-sapping friction between the wheels. Two wheels in a watch movement rarely engage with each other—a wheel engages with not another wheel, but a pinion. In watchmaking language the pinion is a cogwheel with fewer than 15 teeth. A pinion is generally made from polished, hardened steel, whilst the gear wheels are brass (and very rarely from beryllium bronze).

The barrel of a fully wound spring in a wall clock cannot be brought to a standstill with one's

bare hands, but the escape wheel of the same clock can be stopped with a light touch of the finger: "Gear trains convert high torque with a low rotational speed into low torque with a high rotational speed." This example clearly shows how great the loss of power is in a clockwork movement, and how small a force is required to drive the tiny movement within a ladies' watch.

Lots of power for just a short time

A movement without an escapement differs only marginally in the way that it works from the old spring-driven toys that used to be notorious for having to be wound up every couple of minutes, and that now fetch a high price at auction because of their rarity value.

Since there are no gear ratios of 1:1 in the movement (apart from indirectly in the motion work), the speed of rotation changes every time that the gears mesh. At the same time the torque is reduced. Compared with the power that

Girard-Perregaux

Ferrari President, steel, automatic, Girard-Perregaux caliber 2200, from 1999

Gérald Genta

Backtimer, white gold, automatic, base caliber Jaeger-LeCoultre 899 with three-digit countdown day timer, from 1999

Girard-Perregaux

Vintage 1945, steel, rose gold, automatic, Girard-Perregaux caliber 3000, from 1999

Paul Gerber

Model 33 Moon Phase, rose gold, manual wind, Gerber caliber 33 with moon phase display, from 2006

Paul Gerber

Retro Twin, yellow gold, automatic Gerber caliber 15 (base caliber ETA 7001), retrograde second hand, from 2006

Glashütter Uhrenbetrieb GUB

Men's watch 01, yellow gold, manual wind, GUB caliber 28, from 1950

Glashütte Original
Julius Assmann 2, rose gold, manual wind, Glashütte Original caliber 52, watch face from Meissen porcelain, from 1999

Glashütter Uhrenbetrieb GUB
Spezimatic, yellow gold, automatic, GUB caliber 661, from 1955

Glashütte Original
Senator Automatic Panorama Date, rose gold, automatic, Glashütte Original caliber 39-41, from 1999

Glashütte Original
Karree Small Seconds, rose gold, manual wind, Glashütte Original caliber 42-05, from 1999

Glashütte Original
1845 Régulateur, rose gold, manual wind, Glashütte Original caliber 49-04, from 1999

Glashütte Original
Senator Automatic, rose gold, automatic, Glashütte Original caliber 39-10, from 1999

arrives at the escape wheel, the torque delivered to the barrel by the mainspring is enormous.

The change in rotational speed between the barrel and the escape wheel is also very great. By the time the ponderous barrel has made just one revolution, the harassed escape wheel has already completed hundreds. It is therefore highly possible for a delicate escape wheel pivot to be simply ripped off by its own speed if the fully wound movement runs unchecked, particularly if the oil film surrounding it is no longer perfect.

Without an escapement, or more precisely without the escape lever, a fully wound movement would run down within a very short time. With a watch this takes less than a minute, while with a clock it can take as much as half an hour. So on the one hand, the escapement checks the uncontrolled, fast

running of the train. On the other hand, it transfers the by now greatly reduced power from the mainspring, which has been transmitted through the gear train, to the oscillating system.

The escapement

The German term for the escapement is *die Hemmung*, which means "inhibition," and in the same way as the suggestion that a person should "not have any inhibitions" could lead to dire consequences, the effect of a watch losing its inhibitions—its escapement—would be equally catastrophic. It is the escapement that turns a spring-driven mechanism into a device for measuring time. It is at one and the same time a driver and something that is driven.

The escapement consists of an escape lever and an escape wheel. The escape lever is also known

Harwood
Automatic, steel, automatic, ETA caliber 2892-2, winding and adjustment of hands via rotating bezel, from 1999

Glashütte Original
PanoReserve, rose gold, manual wind, Glashütte Original caliber 65-01, power reserve display, from 2006

Glashütte Original
PanoMaticLunar, steel, automatic, Glashütte Original caliber 90-02, moon phase display, from 2006

Harwood
Automatic Louis Reguin, steel, automatic, ETA caliber 2892-2, winding and adjustment of hands via rotating bezel, from 2006

41

Heuer
Abercrombie & Fitch Solunar, steel, manual wind, tidal indicator at six o'clock, from 1948

Hermès
Dressage, red gold, automatic, Vaucher caliber P 1928, from 2006

Hublot
Elegant, yellow gold, automatic, Frédéric Piguet caliber 9511, from 1999

IWC
Men's watch, silver, manual wind, from 1918

as an anchor because of its shape, which generally resembles that of a ship's anchor.

Broadly speaking, the main function of the escapement is to check—to "inhibit"—the rotation of the clockwork wheels. At the same time it is responsible for converting the rotation of the escape wheel into the pendulum motion of the oscillating system (pendulum or balance). Conversely, the oscillating system prevents the escapement from completely stopping the movement, because the pendulum or balance forces the escapement to allow the gear train to rotate, step by step, allowing it to "escape."

In English we talk of the "escapement" and in French the *échappement*, both of which imply "escaping" or "getting free." However the German term *Hemmung* ("inhibition") means the opposite. It is reminiscent of the glass that

IWC
Yacht Club II, steel, automatic, caliber IWC 3254, from 1976

IWC

Engineer SL, yellow gold, automatic, caliber IWC 8541B, protected from magnetic fields by soft iron inner case, from 1973

IWC

Portuguese, steel, manual wind, caliber IWC 982, from 1975

IWC

Men's watch, yellow gold, manual wind, caliber IWC8, from 1941

IWC

Portuguese Automatic, platinum, automatic, IWC caliber 887/2, from 1999

IWC

Engineer, steel, automatic, caliber IWC 8531, only 250 pieces were manufactured with this watch face, from 1960

IWC
Engineer Automatic, steel, automatic, IWC caliber 80110, protected from magnetic fields by soft iron inner case, from 2006

IWC
Portofino Automatic, red gold, IWC caliber 30110 (base caliber ETA 2892-A2), from 2006

IWC
Portuguese Automatic, white gold, automatic, IWC caliber 50010, eight-day power reserve, from 2006

Jaeger-LeCoultre
Men's watch with digital display, rose gold, manual wind, JLC caliber 480CW, from 1950

Jaeger-LeCoultre
Reverso, steel, manual wind, JLC caliber, from 1935

Jaeger-LeCoultre
Master Ultrathin, red gold, automatic, JLC caliber 849, from 1999

Jaeger-LeCoultre
Master Control, red gold, automatic,
JLC caliber 899, from 2006

Jaeger-LeCoultre
LeCoultre Futurematic, yellow gold,
automatic, JLC caliber 497, with
bumper automatic movement and
power reserve display, crown on rear
of the casing, from 1940

Jaeger-LeCoultre
Reverso Grande Date, steel,
manual wind, JLC caliber 875,
power reserve display, from 2006

Jaeger-LeCoultre
Reverso Classique, yellow gold,
manual wind, JLC caliber 846,
from 1999

Jaeger-LeCoultre
Reverso Grande Taille, yellow gold,
manual wind, JLC caliber 822, from
1999

Daniel JeanRichard
TV Screen Automatic, steel,
automatic, JR caliber 24DJR (base
caliber ETA 2824-2), from 1999

JeanRichard
Grand TV Screen Double Retrograde,
rose gold, automatic, JR caliber 23
(base caliber ETA 2892-A2),
retrograde date and seconds display,
from 2006

Junghans
Chronometer, high-grade steel,
manual wind, Junghans caliber
62.1, from 1960

Junghans
Max Bill, steel, manual
wind, ETA caliber 2801-2,
from 1999

Kelek
Automatic with power reserve, steel, automatic, Kelek caliber 7000
(base caliber ETA 2892-A2), power reserve display, from 1999

Kurth
Skeleton watch, rose gold, manual wind, historic ETA caliber from
the 1940s, from 1999

Maurice Lacroix
Jumping hour, steel/yellow gold, manual wind, caliber ML 28 (base caliber Peseux 7046), from 1999

Maurice Lacroix
Tiago skeleton watch, steel, automatic, caliber ML14 (base caliber ETA 2892-2), from 1999

A. Lange & Söhne
Men's watch, yellow gold, manual wind, Lange caliber 10 ½'', from 1944

Maurice Lacroix
Pontos Réserve de Marche, steel, automatic, ETA caliber 2897, power reserve display, from 2006

is half full or half empty, depending upon whether one is an optimist or a pessimist—identical contents, but different points of view. The German clock is inhibited or checked; the English or French clock is freed. But, realistically speaking, English and French clocks do also have to be inhibited, as it's only at that point that something is also allowed to run away—namely the gear train.

And despite its "inhibitions," it still runs at a fast and furious pace. In one hour, the escape wheel of a modern mechanical movement completes 28,800 little steps. The pallet is flung backwards and forwards by the unremitting balance exactly the same number of times as the steps, with repeatedly renewed vigor. In comparison with a car engine this is, of course, still a snail's pace. However, if one considers that the barrel barely moves in one hour, the increase in speed is quite considerable.

With the majority of today's escapement mechanisms the all-important braking of the train is accomplished by two "claws" (pallets) on the anchor, which alternately engage the teeth of the escape wheel, thereby stopping it from turning. The anchor is a lever with two

A. Lange & Söhne
Men's watch, yellow gold, manual wind, Lange shaped movement, from 1932

A. Lange & Söhne
Langematik, white gold, automatic,
Lange caliber L921.2, from 1999

A. Lange & Söhne
1815 Up and Down, yellow gold, manual
wind, Lange caliber L942.1, from 1999

A. Lange & Söhne
Cabaret, yellow gold, manual wind,
Lange caliber L931.3, from 1999

A. Lange & Söhne
1815 Automatic, yellow gold, automatic,
Lange caliber L921.2, from 2006

A. Lange & Söhne
Saxonia, yellow gold, manual wind,
Lange caliber L941.3, from 2006

A. Lange & Söhne
Lange 1, yellow gold, manual wind,
Lange caliber L901.0, from 1999

Limes
Pharo Power Reserve, steel, manual wind, ETA caliber 7001 with Soprod power reserve module, from 2006

A. Lange & Söhne
1815, white gold, manual wind, Lange caliber L941.1, from 2006

A. Lange & Söhne
Cabaret, yellow gold, manual wind, Lange caliber L931.3, from 2006

A. Lange & Söhne
Langematik, yellow gold, automatic, Lange caliber L921.4 SAX-O-MAT, from 2006

Longines
Men's watch, steel, manual wind, Longine caliber 13.34 with enamel face, from 1915

49

Longines
Doctor's Watch, steel, manual wind,
Longines caliber 9.32, shaped
movement, from 1931

Longines
Master Collection Automatic,
steel, automatic, Longines
caliber L619 (base caliber ETA
2892-A2), from 2006

Longines
Mystérieuse, white gold, manual wind, Longines caliber 237,
hour display via central rotating disc, from 1957

Longines
Hour Glass, steel/gold-plated,
manual wind, Longines caliber 9.LT,
from 1954

Jean Marcel
Mystery Tonneau World Map, steel, automatic, ETA caliber 2824
with Jean Marcel module, revolving face with digital jumping hour,
from 1999

Jean Marcel
Automatic, steel, automatic, ETA caliber 2688,
from 1999

Braking claws

limbs made from hardened steel (or, in clocks, from brass and steel). The axis of rotation of the anchor lies at the point of intersection of the vertical and horizontal shafts.

The pallets of watch anchors are synthetic rubies that are inset into the steel body of the anchor and fixed with a tiny drop of shellac or, more often nowadays, with a special glue.

Driven by spring power or a weight, the escape wheel just wants to turn. So it finds the pallets that keep sticking between its teeth extremely aggravating. There is always an escape tooth in contact with one of the anchor pallets, or more specifically with the "locking face" on the edge of the pallet.

As the pendulum swings, the anchor also has to perform the same movement. As it does so, the

MeisterSinger
Edition Scrypto 1Z, manual wind, ETA caliber 6497-1, hour display only, from 2006

51

Mido
Commander Chronometer, steel,
automatic, ETA caliber 2836-2,
from 2006

Minerva
Pythagore Anniversary, steel, manual wind,
Minerva caliber 48, from 1999

Milus
Xephios, steel, automatic, ETA caliber
2836-2, from 2006

point of one of the escape teeth—which is continuously pressing against the pallet—slides from its locking face on the side to the impulse face on the front of the pallet.

At last the escape wheel has the opportunity to move itself slightly. The escape tooth contacts the well-lubricated impulse face of the releasing pallet, giving it an upward push at the same time as pushing the anchor further away from its original position. The arms of the anchor transfer the impulse via the shaft, at the end of which is a small fork with a notch. In this way the anchor provides the pendulum with the small amount of momentum needed for it to swing steadily. Then the escape tooth slips off the impulse face of the pallet (an action termed "the drop") and, on the opposite side of the anchor, another of the escape teeth engages with the locking face of the second pallet and remains at rest until released.

For obvious reasons a pendulum is unsuitable for a portable clock. So the inventor of the pocket watch was confronted with the task of designing a clock that could perform its

Movado
Polyplan, white gold,
manual wind, Movado
caliber 400, from
1930

Movado
SE Automatic, steel, automatic,
ETA caliber 2892-A2, from 2006

Movado
Men's watch, steel, manual wind,
Movado caliber 261, from 1945

Movado
Viziomatic, steel,
auto-quartz, ETA caliber
205.911, from 1999

Movado
Museum Watch Safiro Limited Edition,
rose gold, manual wind, Frédéric
Piguet caliber 21P, from 1999

Franck Muller
Cintrée Curvex Seconde Rétrograde,
white gold, automatic, FM caliber
7500, from 1999

Movado
Botelo Automatic, steel,
automatic, ETA caliber 2824-2,
from 2006

Franck Muller
Cintrée Curvex Jumping Hour, yellow gold, automatic, FM caliber 7500, from 1999

Franck Muller
Long Island, white gold, automatic, FM caliber 2800, from 2006

Nouvelle Horologie Calabrese
Analogica, steel, automatic, ETA caliber 2892-A2 modified by Vincent Calabrese, digital hour display with minute index, from 2006

Nienaber
King Size RetroLator, steel, manual wind, AS caliber 1130, jumping minute hand, jumping hour hand, from 2006

Omega
Seamaster Railmaster XXL Chronometer, steel, automatic, Omega caliber 2201 (base caliber ETA 6498), C.O.S.C. certified chronometer, from 2006

function in any position, a clock that would still show the time if its wearer was doing a head-stand—provided that it didn't fall out of his waistcoat pocket while he was doing so!

The solution to the problem of returning the regulating device to its neutral position without relying exclusively on the force of gravity came a step closer with the invention of the balance spring. We can credit this enormous leap forward in the development of the pocket watch to an ingenious Dutchman, Christiaan Huygens, who in 1675 was the first person to bend a thin, flexible wire into a spiral and use it to operate a regulating device.

The next stage of development on the quest to design a robust, less sensitive precision watch, a variation of which we are still using at the beginning of the twenty-first century, was

Nomos
Tangente Date Power Reserve, steel, manual wind, Nomos caliber Delta with power reserve display, from 2006

Nomos
Orion, steel, manual wind, ETA caliber Peseux 7001, from 1999

Nomos
Tetra, steel, manual wind, Nomos caliber Alpha, from 2006

Omega
Seamaster XVI, red gold, automatic, Omega caliber 471, special model for the 16th Olympic Games in Melbourne, from 1956

Nomos
Tangente, steel, manual wind, Nomos caliber Alpha, from 2006

Omega

Men's watch, yellow gold, manual wind, Omega caliber 302, from 1955

Omega

De Ville Tonneau, steel, automatic, Omega caliber 1120 (base caliber ETA 2892-A2), C.O.S.C. certified chronometer, from 1999

Omega

Seamaster Automatic Chronometer, yellow gold, automatic, Omega caliber 751, C.O.S.C. certified chronometer, from 1956

Omega

Seamaster Omegamatic, steel, uni-directional rotating diving bezel, quartz with automatic wind, Omega caliber 1400 (base caliber ETA 205.111), from 1999

Oris

Rectangular Classic, Oris caliber 583 (base caliber 2688/2671), from 1999

Oris

Big Crown Pointer Date, steel, automatic, Oris caliber 654 (base caliber ETA 2824-2), from 2006

the invention of the "free anchor" or "detached lever" escapement by the English watchmaker Thomas Mudge (1715–1794).

The crucial difference between the "detached" lever escapement and other kinds of escapement is that, in the case of the latter, the pendulum or balance wheel is linked permanently and inseparably to the escapement and is therefore always subject to interference from the movement. This means that although the oscillating system is supplied with power, the permanent link causes it to be simultaneously deprived of that power again. The balance wheel in the escapement invented by Mudge has no such problems. After the balance wheel has received the impulse from the anchor, it is completely free—hence the name of "free" anchor escapement. This is actually a bit misleading, since it is not the escapement but the balance wheel that is "freed."

Panerai

Radiomir base, steel, manual wind, Panerai caliber OP X, C.O.S.C. certified chronometer, from 2006

Officine Panerai

Luminor Marina, steel, manual wind, ETA caliber 6497-2, C.O.S.C. certified chronometer, from 1999

Officine Panerai

Luminor Submersible, titanium, automatic, ETA caliber 7750, from 1999

Parmigiani

Kalpa XL Hebdomadaire, steel, manual wind, Parmigiani caliber 110, eight-day power reserve, from 2006

57

Parmigiani
Bugatti 370 Type, steel, manual wind, Parmigiani caliber 370, ten-day power reserve, from 2006

Péquignet
Moorea Power Reserve, steel/yellow gold, automatic, ETA caliber 2892-2 with module for power reserve display, from 1999

Patek Philippe
Calatrava, yellow gold, manual wind, Patek Philippe caliber 91, from 1953

Patek Philippe
Art Deco men's watch, white gold, manual wind, Patek Philippe caliber 10, from 1928

Patek Philippe
Men's watch, yellow gold, manual wind, Patek Philippe caliber 10, from 1932

Patek Philippe
Asymmétrique, yellow gold, manual
wind, Patek Philippe caliber 91,
from 1935

Patek Philippe
Men's watch for Gübelin, yellow
gold, manual wind, Patek Philippe
caliber 9-90, from 1951

Patek Philippe
Men's watch, white gold,
automatic, Patek Philippe caliber
1-350, from 1976

The oscillating system

With the introduction of the balance wheel, the watchmaker was confronted with all sorts of problems that he had never previously encountered. While the pendulum of a wall clock or grandfather clock always has the same oscillation amplitude (provided that there is an even power supply, e.g. through weight propulsion), and can generally continue its work unimpeded by outside influences (apart, perhaps, from fluctuations in air pressure and temperature), the balance wheel of a wristwatch is subject to a whole range of adversities that can interfere with the accurate running of the watch. It is not gentle, gliding motions that affect the balance wheel, but the persistent short, sharp movements that occur when changing between a sloping position and the vertical or horizontal. The watch and, by default, the balance wheel have to withstand this rough handling in humid tropical climates or icy cold conditions, when diving or when mountain climbing.

Patek Philippe
Moon Phase, yellow gold, automatic,
Patek Philippe caliber 240/154,
moon phase and power reserve
display, from 1999

Perrelet
Dipteros/Temptest, steel, automatic,
Perrelet caliber DH95, from 1999

Patek Philippe
Calatrava, yellow gold, automatic,
Patek Philippe caliber 240PS,
from 1999

Patek Philippe
Neptune, yellow gold,
automatic, Patek Philippe
caliber 315/190, from 1999

Patek Philippe
Aquanaut, steel, automatic, Patek
Philippe caliber 330/194, from 1999

Patek Philippe
Gondolo, yellow gold, automatic,
Patek Philippe caliber 315/190,
from 1999

Patek Philippe
Calatrava Grande Taille, yellow gold,
automatic, Patek Philippe caliber
315SC, from 2006

Piaget
Tradition, white gold, automatic,
Piaget caliber 190P, C.O.S.C. certified
chronometer, from 1999

Patek Philippe
Nautilus, steel, automatic, Patek Philippe caliber
330/194, from 1999

Patek Philippe
Nautilus, steel, automatic, Patek Philippe
caliber 240 PS IRM C LU, moon phase and
power reserve display, from 2006

Piaget
Tradition, white gold, automatic,
Piaget caliber 190P, C.O.S.C. certified
chronometer, from 1999

Patek Philippe
Gondolo, white gold, manual wind, Patek
Philippe caliber 215 PS, from 2006

There is no other technical mechanism that is permanently subjected to such constant stress as the watch. Year in, year out, this test of stamina is endured by these little machines which contain screws so tiny that 10,000 of them would not fill a single thimble. Little machines in which a metal spiral spring coils and uncoils almost 30,000 times (sometimes more) in one hour, a spring which is so thin it makes a hair from a human head look like a rope next to it. Little machines whose turning parts are lubricated with an amount of oil which is barely perceptible even when viewed through a magnifying glass.

If subjected to similar treatment, a car would be ready for the garbage heap within the space of a few hours. We expect absolute precision from a wristwatch for years. A watch running with a rate deviation of ten seconds per day is working with a tolerance of approximately 0.1 per mille!

Piaget
Légende Rectangle à l'Ancienne,
white gold, manual wind, Piaget
caliber 9P2, from 1999

Piaget
Polo, white gold, automatic, Piaget caliber 500P, from 1999

Paul Picot
Atelier 1100 Régulateur, steel, automatic, PP caliber 1100 (base caliber ETA 2892-A2), C.O.S.C. certified chronometer, power reserve display, from 1999

Piaget
Altiplano ultrathin, white gold, manual wind, Piaget caliber 430P, from 2006

Paul Picot
Firshire 1937, white gold, manual wind, PP caliber 88 (base caliber ETA C735 from 1937), power reserve display, from 1999

Piaget
Emperador retrograde second, white gold, automatic, Piaget caliber 560P, from 2006

This is something you should consider carefully before you ask the watchmaker to adjust a watch that is gaining maybe half a minute a week. Or if, after maybe three or five years of reliable service, a wristwatch needs a check-up and general service.

The run to the banking and uneven teeth

The balance wheel receives an impulse from the fork of the escape lever, which brings it out of its resting position and sets it in motion. At the same time, the escape lever is made to move towards the banking pins after an escape tooth has given impulse to one of the pallets as it drops from the impulse face. Watchmakers call this movement the "run to the banking." In general, banking pins are no longer used in modern clocks. Instead, the anchor moves within a countersunk dip in the base plate.

The "run to the banking" is also an important safety device in the escapement, because it

Paul Picot
Firshire Tonneau 3000 Retrograde, steel, automatic, PP caliber 1300 (base caliber ETA 2892-A2), from 1999

Rado
Anatom, tungsten-titanium carbide, automatic, ETA caliber 2671, from 1999

Rado
Sintra XXL, ceramic, automatic, ETA caliber 2892-A2, from 2006

Revue Thommen
Specialties SK, steel, automatic, Revue Thommen caliber GT54, skeleton movement, from 2006

Rado
Original, steel, automatic, ETA caliber 2824-2, from 2006

Auguste Reymond
Ragtime Power Reserve, steel,
automatic, AR caliber 9035 (base
caliber ETA 2892), power reserve
display, from 1999

Auguste Reymond
Boogie Gold Edition, red gold, manual
wind, ETA caliber 6425, from 2006

Roamer
Compétence Original Type 2, steel, manual
wind, FHF caliber 138.011, from 2006

64

Robergé
Andromède RS Régulateur, steel, automatic, Paul Picot caliber 1000 (base caliber Nouvelle Lémania), from 1999

Rolex
Oyster Perpetual Milgauss, steel, automatic, Rolex caliber 1066M, C.O.S.C. certified chronometer, protected from magnetic fields by soft iron inner case, from 1958

Rolex
Oyster Perpetual Chronometer, steel, automatic, Rolex caliber, also called the "Bubble Back" because of its slightly domed base, from 1948

Rolex
Men's watch, yellow gold, manual wind, Rolex caliber, from 1930

Rolex
Oyster Perpetual Chronometer, rose gold, automatic, Rolex caliber, also called the "Bubble Back" because of its slightly domed base, with original Mickey Mouse face, from 1949

Rolex
Prince Brancard Chronometer "Extraprima Observatory Quality," steel, manual wind, Rolex caliber, from 1935

65

Rolex
Oyster Perpetual Air-King, steel, automatic, Rolex caliber 3130 (base caliber Rolex 3135), C.O.S.C. certified chronometer, from 2006

guarantees that all the escape teeth can drop safely, even if they are not all of a uniform length. So if a tooth is a little too long, the escape lever is simply moved a little further, with the "run to the banking" serving as additional maneuvering room.

The oscillation amplitude of the balance wheel is, of course, dependent upon the impulse given to it; i.e. the balance wheel of a fully wound watch makes larger oscillations than those of a watch that has almost run down.

Rolex
Prince, rose gold, manual wind, Rolex caliber 7040-2, C.O.S.C. certified chronometer, from 2006

Rolex
Oyster Turn-O-Graph, steel, automatic, Rolex caliber 3135, C.O.S.C. certified chronometer, from 2006

Rolex
Oyster Perpetual Day-Date, rose gold, automatic, Rolex caliber 3155 (base caliber Rolex 3135), C.O.S.C. certified chronometer, from 2006

Rolex
Prince Brancard Chronometer Jumping Hours, white gold, manual wind, jumping hour display, from 1945

Daniel Roth
Rétrograde, yellow gold, manual wind, Lémania caliber 27NL reworked by Daniel Roth, from 1999

Daniel Roth
GMT, steel, automatic, Girard-Perregaux caliber GP 3100 reworked by Daniel Roth, second time zone digitally displayed, from 1999

Jörg Schauer
Day Date Zentral, steel, automatic, ETA caliber 2836, from 2006

Jörg Schauer
Digital 1, steel, automatic, PUW caliber 1560D, time displayed on three concentric dials, from 1999

Jörg Schauer
Kleine Schauer, steel, automatic, ETA caliber 2824, from 2006

Stowa
Antea, steel, manual wind, ETA caliber
Peseux 7001, from 2006

Otto Schlund
Classic with date display, steel, automatic,
ETA caliber 2824-2, from 2006

Alain Silberstein
24 H, steel, automatic, base caliber ETA
2892-A2 reworked by Alain Silberstein,
24-hour time display, from 1999

Seiko
Spring Drive, steel, automatic, Seiko caliber 5R65,
patented electromagnetic escapement system
"Tri-syncro regulator," from 2006

When and why a clock runs accurately

One question that we haven't answered yet: How do you make a watch go faster, slower, or, in an ideal world, just right? Of course, this depends on a wide variety of factors. The basic requirements are a clean and well-lubricated movement, a mainspring that supplies as constant a torque as possible, a train with cleanly cut and perfectly mounted wheels, an accurately working escapement and, of course, a well-adjusted balance made from

Tissot
Men's watch, steel, manual wind,
caliber 20, from 1935

69

Tissot
Heritage Gold, red gold, automatic, ETA caliber 2895, C.O.S.C. certified chronometer, from 1999

Ulysse Nardin
San Marco Chronometer Venezia, yellow gold, automatic, base caliber ETA 2892, face made from cloisonné enamel, limited edition of 35 copies, from 1999

Ulysse Nardin
San Marco Chronometer Golden Hind, yellow gold, automatic, base caliber ETA 2892, face made from cloisonné enamel, limited edition of 25 copies, from 1999

Ulysse Nardin
Maxi Marine Chronometer, red gold, automatic, Ulysse Nardin caliber UN 26 (base caliber ETA 2892), C.O.S.C. certified chronometer, from 1999

Ulysse Nardin
Marine Chronometer, yellow gold, automatic, Ulysse Nardin caliber UN 26 (base caliber ETA 2892), C.O.S.C. certified chronometer, from 1999

non-magnetizable materials that are barely susceptible to changes in temperature.

Particularly high-quality watches that fulfill these requirements perfectly are regulated with just two tiny screws or small adjusting weights that are set into the balance rim and are pulled out a little when the watch is going too fast, or twisted in when it runs too slowly. Examples of this are the Gyromax balance by Patek Philippe and the MicroStella screws on the Rolex balances.

Curb pins and hands

However, most clocks rely on a different method of regulation, which uses curb pins and a regulator. In order for the watchmaker to carry

Union
Tradition Automatic, steel,
automatic, Union caliber 26-11,
from 1999

Union
Classic Power Reserve, steel,
automatic, Union caliber
26-44, from 2006

Union
Tradition Regulator, steel,
automatic, Union caliber 26-42,
from 1999

Urban Jürgensen & Sønner
Referenz 5, yellow gold, automatic,
from 1999

Urban Jürgensen & Sønner
Referenz 6, yellow gold, manual wind,
from 1999

71

Vacheron Constantin
Men's watch, red gold, manual wind,
Vacheron Constantin caliber,
from 1933

Vacheron Constantin
Automatic men's watch, red gold, manual wind, Vacheron
Constantin caliber 1072, from 1963

Vacheron Constantin
Les Historiques Rectangle, yellow gold, manual wind, Vacheron
Constantin caliber 1017, from 1999

Vacheron Constantin
Overseas, steel, automatic, Vacheron Constantin caliber
1310, from 1999

Vacheron Constantin
Montre à volets, yellow and white
gold, manual wind, blind in front of
the face operated by a second crown
at the nine o'clock position, Vacheron
Constantin caliber, from 1930

out very slight adjustments to the regulation, many watches feature what is known as a regulator hand. This is located opposite the curb pins, and both it and the regulator are generally made from a single piece of metal or are held together by friction.

The regulator hand, the regulator, and the curb pins work according to the same principle as the two-armed lever. This means that the watchmaker has to push the regulator hand in the opposite direction to that which he requires for the curb pins. This is generally simplified by the + and − symbols or letters "A" and "R" milled into the balance cock, whereby "A" (from the French, *avancer*, meaning "advance") makes the watch run faster and "R" (from the French, *retarder*, meaning "delay") makes it run slower.

Vacheron Constantin
Toledo 1952, white gold, automatic,
Vacheron Constantin caliber 1125,
full calendar with moon phase
display, from 2006

Vacheron Constantin
Overseas, steel, automatic, Vacheron
Constantin caliber 1126, from 2006

Vacheron Constantin
Les Complications Saltarello, white
gold, automatic, Vacheron
Constantin caliber 1120MR, jumping
hour hand display, retrograde
minute display, from 1999

Vulcain
Men's watch, silver, manual wind,
from 1925

73

Raymond Weil
Classic, steel, automatic, ETA caliber
2824-2, from 1999

Zenith
Port-Royal Chronometer, steel,
manual wind, Zenith caliber 135,
from 1965

Raymond Weil
Parsifal Réserve de Marche, steel,
automatic, RW caliber 3500 (base
caliber ETA 2892-A2), from 2006

Raymond Weil
Parsifal Automatic, steel, automatic,
ETA 2824-2, from 1999

Xemex
Offroad, steel, automatic,
ETA caliber 2824-2, from 1999

Xemex
Avenue, steel, automatic, ETA caliber
2892-A2, from 1999

Zenith
Chronomaster Elite HW, steel, manual
wind, Zenith caliber 684 Elite, power
reserve display, from 1999

Zenith
Port-Royal Rectangle Elite, steel,
automatic, Zenith caliber 684 Elite,
from 2006

Occasionally the abbreviations "F" and "S" for "fast" and "slow" are also used.

There are various design features which make it easier to carry out very slight adjustments to the regulation of a watch; for instance, extremely long regulator hands (large displacement on the hand—small displacement on the regulator). Adjustment of the regulator might also be done by direct or indirect use of a micrometer screw (swan's neck fine regulation device). Incidentally, a watch that gains five minutes a day is working very accurately; it just needs to be precisely regulated.

2.

CHRONO-GRAPHS

A chronograph saves you from having to take constant glances at a watch when measuring short intervals of time. And when the timing of sporting events was still done by hand, it was also an extremely practical tool. Today the chronograph is first and foremost a sophisticated boy's toy, useful, for instance, for checking the grilling time for steaks. However, watchmakers and watch designers still devote an enormous amount of effort to it.

Angelus
Chronograph, yellow gold, manual
wind with column wheel operation,
from 1945

Audemars Piguet
Chronograph, yellow gold, manual
wind with column wheel operation,
from 1949

Audemars Piguet
Royal Oak Offshore Chronograph,
steel, automatic, AP caliber
2226/2840, from 2006

Baume & Mercier
Malibu Chronograph, steel,
automatic, BM caliber 13750 (base
caliber ETA 750), from 1999

Baume & Mercier
CapeLand, steel, automatic,
ETA caliber 7750, from 1999

Baume & Mercier
Classima Chronograph, steel,
automatic, BM caliber 13283 (base
caliber Lémania 283), from 1999

Baume & Mercier
Milleis Chronograph, rose gold,
manual wind, caliber Lémania 1870,
from 1999

Ｗith the invention of the clock, man fulfilled his desire to divide the time of the day into periods that were as even as possible. This ambition satisfied, in the nineteenth century he began to aspire toward being able to measure and even record short intervals of time, irrespective of the time of day.

You can, of course, measure a journey from A to B by constantly looking at your watch. But this is extremely inconvenient and not without its dangers if sitting behind a steering wheel.

Fortunately for us, inventive watchmakers have provided us with as practical an instrument as the chronograph for just such a contingency, a tool that enables us to measure a short period of time by simply pressing a button, without needing to pay too much attention.

Time writer without a writing instrument

The term chronograph comes from the Greek and is formed from the stems *chronos* "time" and *graphô* ("I write"). Now, you could justifiably argue that the term Chrono-"Graph" is no longer appropriate for today's watches with integral stopwatches, because these watches are used for neither writing nor taking records. But remember that we also still talk

about "steamers," even though large ships have been powered by diesel engines or gas turbines for decades, and that it's a long time since a car's "mudguards" have carried out the function implied by their name. The first chronograph really was a time writer. In 1820, the French watchmaker, Rieussec, invented a watch that, when a mechanism was activated, wrote on the watch face with an ink pen secured to the wrist.

In 1831, Austrian-born watchmaker Joseph Thaddäus Winnerl—a former employee of the watchmaking genius, Abraham Louis Breguet who had died in 1823 invented a watch, the second hand of which could be stopped and restarted whenever required, independently of the clockwork movement. A crucial drawback to Winnerl's design was the extremely slow return of the second hand to the zero position at the end of a measurement.

In 1862, this problem was overcome by Adolphe Nicole from the Joux Valley (French Switzerland), who developed the first chronographs with hands that could be instantly reset. To achieve this, Nicole fixed a heart-shaped cam onto the arbor of the second hand.

When the chronograph hand was reset to zero, a spring-loaded lever operated laterally against this cam, which has remained virtually unchanged to the present day, and because of its characteristic shape is known by watchmakers simply as the "heart piece." When struck by the impact of this "violent" lever, the heart piece is forced to reverberate back and forth until the flats of the heart cams rest against this lever, the heart piece lever.

Bertolucci
Vir Chronograph, steel, automatic, ETA caliber 7750, from 1999

Baume & Mercier
CapeLand S Chronograph, steel, automatic, BM caliber 13750 (base caliber ETA 7750), from 2006

Blancpain
Chronograph 2100, yellow gold, automatic, from 1999

Masculine characteristics: an arrangement of high-quality chronographs from Officine Panerai, Zenith and Blancpain

Blancpain
Léman Chrono Flyback Large Date, steel, automatic, Blancpain caliber 69F8, from 2006

81

Rainer Brand
Carcassonne, steel, automatic,
Lémania caliber 1352, from 1999

Fourth wheel—second purpose

The chronograph mechanism is generally driven by the fourth wheel.

There are various options for transferring the power from the fourth wheel, which rotates within the actual movement—i.e. between the plates—to the chronograph movement. In the traditional design, the chronograph movement is situated on the rear wheel train bridge and so is outside the actual clock movement.

A common method for transmitting the drive is by mounting two long pivots on to the arbor of the fourth wheel (turning within the movement). There is already one pivot on the dial side of the movement, which carries the little second hand. On the second long pivot that projects from the wheel train bridge, a removable clamp is used to attach another wheel, the driving wheel. Unlike the wheels of the actual movement, this wheel has triangular teeth. Drive is transmitted via wheels that

interlock with each other, as opposed to wheels engaging with pinions, the usual action in a wheel train.

The external driving wheel, the one that is mounted on to the arbor of the fourth wheel, engages with another wheel (the coupling clutch wheel) with the same teeth, which sits on a moving lever called the coupling clutch lever.

The coupling clutch lever can rotate slightly round a pivot above the wheel train bridge. A second pivot with a large head and a lug beneath it, which is bolted into the mechanism plate via an oval hole in the coupling lever, determines the range of movement. A small spring (the coupling clutch spring) pushes the coupling lever towards the center. This results in the wheel on top of it—the coupling wheel—meshing with the chronograph center wheel, the teeth of which are only half the size, but identically shaped. So when the start button on the watchcase is pressed, the blocking lever moves out of the way. At the same time, the

Rainer Brand
Kerala, steel, automatic, ETA caliber
7750, from 2006

Breguet
Split-Seconds Chronograph, yellow
gold, manual wind, Breguet caliber
533 NT, from 1999

Automatic movement
from a Glashütte Original
chronograph

Breguet
Marine Chronograph, platinum,
manual wind, Breguet caliber 576,
from 1999

Breguet
Heritage Chronograph, steel,
automatic, Breguet caliber 550,
from 2006

83

Breitling
Chronograph Football
Reference 2734.3, steel,
manual wind, Valjoux caliber
7731, from 1975

Breitling
Chronograph Pupitre Reference
7101.3, steel, manual wind, Valjoux
caliber 7750, from 1975

Breitling
Split-Second Chronograph
Reference 762, steel, manual wind,
with 45-minute counter, from 1950

Breitling
Chronograph Sprint Reference 2018,
steel, manual wind, Valjoux caliber
7733, from 1975

Breitling
Chrono-Matic Reference 2112-15,
steel, automatic, caliber 15,
from 1969

Breitling
Crosswind, steel, automatic,
Breitling caliber 13 (base
caliber ETA 7750), from 1999

Breitling
Montbrillant Olympus, steel, automatic, Breitling caliber 19 (base caliber ETA 2892-A2), from 2006

Bulova
Doctor's Watch, steel/gold-plated, manual wind, FHF caliber 138.001, from 1999

Breitling
Chronomat Evolution, steel, automatic, Breitling caliber 13 (base caliber ETA 7750), C.O.S.C. certified chronometer, from 2006

Bunz
Chronograph, platinum, automatic, ETA caliber 7750, from 2006

Bulgari
Assioma Chrono, yellow gold,
automatic, ETA caliber 2094,
from 2006

Bulgari
Bulgari Rattrapante, yellow gold,
automatic, Bulgari caliber MVA 900
(base caliber GP 8290), from 1999

Cartier
Pasha de Cartier, steel, automatic,
Cartier caliber 205 (base caliber
Frédéric Piguet 1185), from 1999

coupling lever moves towards the center, causing the coupling wheel to engage the chronograph center wheel. The chronograph begins its task of measuring a short interval of time. This design enables the chronograph mechanism to be turned on and off as required.

If the interval being measured lasts for longer than one minute, the minutes counting wheel, which operates the 30-minute counter in front of the clock's dial, has to be advanced by one step. To do this, an arm that is also mounted on to the arbor of the chronograph center wheel

meshes with the teeth of the intermediate wheel, which in turn interlocks with the minutes counting wheel. The intermediate wheel is advanced by one tooth. Because they have the same teething, the minutes counting wheel also advances by one tooth. At the same time, on the other side of the works, on the front of the dial, the hand of the 30-minute counter advances by exactly one graduation mark.

This is facilitated by a small locking spring (minute count-wheel spring), which meshes with

Cartier

Roadster Chronograph, steel/yellow gold, automatic, Cartier caliber 8510 (base caliber ETA 2894), from 2006

Certina

DS 2 Chronolympic, steel, manual wind, caliber Valjoux 726, from 1975

Certina

DS-3 Chronograph, steel, automatic, Certina caliber 674 (base caliber ETA 7750), from 2006

Philippe Charriol

Supersports Chronograph, steel, automatic, ETA caliber 7750, from 1999

Chopard

Imperiale Chronograph, steel, automatic, Lémania caliber 283, from 1999

87

Chronoswiss
Chronograph-Chronometer, steel, automatic, Chronoswiss caliber C.754 (base caliber ETA 7750), from 1999

Optical delectation: Chronoswiss Chronoscope with visible column wheel, reference number CH 1523 rc, from 2006

Chronoswiss
Pathos, platinum, automatic, Chronoswiss caliber C.732S (base caliber ETA 7750), movement completely skeletonized, from 2006

Chronoswiss
Classic Chronograph, steel, automatic, Chronoswiss caliber C.741 (base caliber ETA 7750), from 2006

the teeth of the minutes counting wheel, only allowing it to advance by one tooth. Finally the wheel is held exactly in position by the minute count-wheel spring until the chronograph center wheel again "sweeps" all the wheels along.

At the end of the timing process, another button is pushed and the coupling lever jumps back, releases its mesh and the blocking lever moves against the chronograph wheel to stop it.

Cyma
Chronograph, silver, manual wind, from 1920

Du Bois & Fils
Chronographe Classique, yellow gold, manual wind, Nouvelle Lémania caliber 1873, from 2006

Corum
Classical Flyback Big Date, steel, automatic, caliber CO 996 (base caliber ETA 2892-A2), C.O.S.C. certified chronometer, from 2006

De Bethune
Monokrone Chronograph, white gold, manual wind, caliber DB 5008 (base caliber LIP 5000), chronograph push button in the crown, from 2006

Dior
Chiffre Rouge Chronograph A02, steel, automatic, ETA caliber 2894-2, from 2006

Dubey & Schaldenbrand
Trial, rose gold, automatic, ETA caliber 7750 with Tricompax display, from 1999

Dubey & Schaldenbrand
Flyback, rose gold, automatic,
ETA caliber 7750 with split-second
chronograph design, from 1999

Dubey & Schaldenbrand
Aerochrono, rose gold, automatic,
ETA caliber 2094, from 2006

Roger Dubuis
S.A.W. Easy Diver, steel, manual wind,
RD caliber 56, from 2006

Ebel
Le Modulor, steel, automatic, Ebel caliber 137,
C.O.S.C. certified chronometer, from 1999

Ebel
1911 Chronograph, rose gold,
automatic, Ebel caliber 137, C.O.S.C.
certified chronometer, from 2006

Eberhard
Split-Second Chronograph
Extra-fort, yellow gold, manual wind
with dual column wheel operation,
from 1945

Eberhard
Replica 2 Counter, silver/gold-plated,
manual wind, Lémania caliber 1872,
from 1999

Eberhard
Chronomaster, steel, one-way bezel,
automatic, Lémania caliber 5100,
from 1999

Eberhard
Tazio Nuvolari, steel, automatic,
ETA caliber 7750, from 1999

91

Eberhard
Chrono 4, steel, automatic, caliber
EB 200 (base caliber ETA 2894-2),
from 2006

The oscillating pinion

Because this chronograph mechanism is technically complicated and therefore expensive to produce, Edouard Heuer (founder of the Heuer watch brand, which is today manufactured under the TAG Heuer name) invented what is called the oscillating pinion, for which he received a patent in May 1887. The oscillating pinion consists of an arbor with two separate toothed wheel rims. The teeth on the dial side engage with the movement's fourth wheel (bearing the second hand), and those on the opposite side with the chronograph center wheel. To engage (start) or disengage (stop) the

Eberhard
Quadrangolo Chrono Screen, steel, manual wind,
Lémania 1872, from 1999

Eterna
Porsche Design Chronograph, steel,
automatic, ETA caliber 7750,
from 1999

Eterna
Pulsometer Chronograph, yellow gold,
automatic, ETA caliber 2894-2,
from 1999

Eterna
25-year Porsche Design Chronograph,
steel, automatic, ETA caliber 7750,
from 1999

Eterna
1948 Moon Phase Chronograph,
steel, automatic, ETA caliber 7751,
certified chronometer, from 2006

Jacques Etoile
Monaco 72C, steel, manual wind,
Valjoux caliber 72C, from 2006

Jacques Etoile
Silverstone Valjoux 23, sterling silver, manual wind, Valjoux caliber 23, from 2006

Formex
Chrono-Tacho, steel/titanium, automatic, ETA caliber 7754, glass-covered slide rule bezel, from 2006

Girard-Perregaux
Richeville Tonneau Chronograph, red gold, manual wind, Girard-Perregaux caliber 8381, from 1999

Girard-Perregaux
Doctor's Chronograph, yellow gold, manual wind, caliber 281, from 1940

Gérald Genta
Gefica Chronograph, bronze, automatic, ETA caliber 7750, from 1999

teeth, the oscillating pinion is lightly tilted. Today, this ingenious design is as popular as ever—indeed, it is used by today's most widely sold chronograph movement, the ETA 7750 (Valjoux).

Controlled heartbeat

We now reach the last stage in the timing process: resetting to zero. The second case pusher is activated and pushes against the reset-to-zero lever. The chronograph center wheel is released by the brake, which holds it when it is not engaged with the coupling wheel.

The heart piece lever is released and is catapulted by the heart piece spring against the heart pieces on the center wheel and the minutes counting wheel. The wheels jerk into the reset position and are held at zero by the hammers of the heart piece lever. These switching operations take place in a fraction of a second, but certainly not at the same time. If,

Girard-Perregaux
Vintage III, red gold, automatic, Girard-Perregaux caliber 3170, from 1999

Girard-Perregaux
GP 7000 Américaine Chronograph, steel/yellow gold, automatic, Girard-Perregaux caliber 8000, from 1999

Girard-Perregaux
Ferrari 250 GT TdF, steel, automatic, Girard-Perregaux caliber 2280, 24-hour display, from 1999

Girard-Perregaux
Ferrari Chronograph Carbon, steel, automatic, Girard-Perregaux caliber 2280, from 1999

Girard-Perregaux
Ferrari Chronograph, steel, automatic, Girard-Perregaux caliber 2280, from 1999

Girard-Perregaux
Laureato EVO 3, steel, automatic, GP caliber 33CD-AOWA, 24-hour display (dual time zone), from 2006

Girard-Perregaux
Richeville Chronograph Carbon, red gold, automatic, GP caliber 3370 (base caliber GP 3300), from 2006

Glashütte Original
Senator Chronograph, steel, automatic, Glashütte Original caliber 39-30, from 1999

Far right: Watches from small manufacturers can also be technically and visually impressive. Best examples: chronographs from Graham and Temption.

Girard-Perregaux
Ferrari Chronograph F50, steel, automatic, Girard-Perregaux caliber 3170, perpetual calendar, 24-hour display, from 1999

for example, the heart piece lever were to strike the heart piece before the brake had disengaged from the center wheel, the brake, still lying in its engaged position, might damage the extremely fine teeth on the wheel.

The adjustment of the wheels and levers and their mesh with each other is made by turning eccentric screws to adjust the distance of the parts from each other. This calibration is done under strong magnification, preferably using a microscope.

96

Glashütte Original
Senator Chronograph Date, steel, automatic, Glashütte Original caliber 39-32, from 1999

Glashütte Original
PanoMaticChrono, steel, manual wind, Glashütte Original caliber 61, chronograph with Flyback function, from 1999

Glashütte Original
PanoRetroGraph, rose gold, manual wind, Glashütte Original caliber 60, chronograph with Flyback reset function, from 2006

Glashütte Original
Sport Chronograph Senator, steel, automatic, Glashütte Original caliber 10-60, from 1999

Glashütte Original
Sport Evolution Chronograph, steel, automatic, Glashütte Original caliber 39-31, from 2006

98

Graham

Chronofighter Classic, steel, automatic, Graham caliber 1722 (base caliber ETA 7750), release lever on crown for chronograph operation, certified chronometer, from 2006

Gucci

G Chrono, steel, quartz, ETA caliber 251.471H1, from 2006

Graham

Swordfish, steel, automatic, Graham caliber 1726 (base caliber ETA 7750), also with crown and pusher on left side of casing, from 2006

Hanhart

Sirius Chronograph, steel, automatic, ETA caliber 7750, from 2006

99

Michel Herbelin
Newport J-Class Chronograph
Flyback, steel, automatic, LIP caliber
8151 (base caliber ETA 7750),
from 2006

Heuer
Calculator, steel, rotating bezel with slide
rule scale, automatic, caliber 12 with
microrotor, from 1975

Heuer
Montreal, steel, automatic,
caliber 12 with microrotor,
from 1975

Triangular pillars as switches

Of course, there have been considerable
advances in the development of chronograph
technology. For instance, over the last ten years,
the cost factor has led to the introduction
of various chronograph modules that are
mounted on to the dial side of the movement.

Unfortunately, and much to the regret of
devotees of the classic chronograph, this has
resulted in one elaborate detail or another
falling victim to the simplified mechanism.
These details include the column wheel,
although this, in keeping with the recent
return to the sophisticated design of earlier
chronographs, is reappearing in newly
designed modules.

There have always been chronographs without
column wheels, which, from an economical
point of view, are preferable to the more
sophisticated column wheel designs. However,
the chronographs were always mounted on the
reverse side of the movement. The column

Heuer
Monaco, steel, automatic, caliber 12
with microrotor, from 1975

Heuer
Autavia, steel, automatic, caliber 12
with microrotor, from 1975

TAG Heuer caliber 360

Hublot
Chronograph Automatic, platinum,
automatic, Frédéric Piguet caliber
1188, from 1999

Hublot
Big Bang, steel, automatic, caliber
HUB 44 (developed and produced by
La Joux Perret), from 2006

Ikepod

Isopod Chronograph, steel, automatic, ETA caliber 2894-2, C.O.S.C. certified chronometer, from 1999

Ikepod

Hemipode Chronograph, steel, automatic, ETA caliber 7750, 24-hour display, C.O.S.C. certified chronometer, from 1999

IWC

Portuguese Chrono Rattrapante, red gold, automatic, IWC caliber C.76240 (base caliber ETA 7750 with IWC split-second design), from 1999

IWC

Portuguese Chrono Automatic, steel, automatic, IWC caliber C.79240 (base caliber ETA 7750), from 1999 wheel—or pillar wheel—design still stands as the crème de la crème of chronograph mechanisms. The term column wheel derives from the French word *colonne* ("column" or "pillar"). The column wheel coordinates all the other switching functions in the watch's chronograph mechanism. In this design the pillars stand at attention like files on a revolving shelf, on top of a sawtoothed wheel on the wheel train bridge of the chronograph.

The column wheel coordinates the starting, stopping and reset-to-zero functions of the chronograph. When the start pusher, located on the case near the two o'clock position, is pressed, the operating lever gives the column wheel the order, "to advance by one tooth." To carry out the order a small hook on the operating lever meshes with the sawteeth of the column wheel and rotates it around by one tooth, whereupon a powerful blocking spring fixes the new position.

At the same time a beak on the coupling lever, with which the connection to the wheel train is made, alternately engages and disengages between the triangular columns.

IWC
Engineer Chronograph, steel, IWC caliber 79350 (base caliber ETA 7750), from 2006

Daniel JeanRichard
Chronograph Sport Tachymeter, steel, automatic, caliber DJR 25 (base caliber ETA 2824-2), from 1999

Jaeger-LeCoultre
Master Chrono, steel, quartz with mechanical chronograph function, from 1999

Jaeger-LeCoultre
Master Compressor Chronograph, steel, automatic, JLC caliber 751, from 2006

Daniel JeanRichard
Chronograph Classic, steel, automatic, caliber DJR 25 (base caliber ETA 2824-2), from 1999

Daniel JeanRichard
TV Screen Chronograph, steel,
automatic, caliber DJR 25 (base
caliber ETA 2824-2), from 1999

Junghans
Tourneur Chronograph,
steel, automatic,
ETA caliber 7750,
from 1999

Junghans
Chronograph, steel,
manual wind, caliber 88,
from 1950

Daniel JeanRichard
TV Screen Chronoscope, steel,
automatic, JR caliber 25 (base
caliber ETA 2824-2), bidirectional
rotating inner bezel, from 2006

Junghans
Arthur Junghans Ambassador,
gold-plated steel, automatic,
ETA caliber 7750, from 2006

If the coupling lever receives the order to "engage," it slips its beak into the gap between two of the (usually) seven columns on the column wheel. This creates the link between the wheels within the motion work and the chronograph mechanism.

If the start pusher is pressed again, the first part of the operation is repeated; however, this time the beak on the coupling lever is raised up by one of the triangular pillars and disengages the link between the column wheel and the chronograph center wheel. Due to the action of the blocking lever and the minute count-wheel spring, the chronograph hands

Kurth
Chronograph Venus, rose gold, manual wind, Venus caliber 187, from 1999

Maurice Lacroix
Column wheel chronograph, yellow gold, manual wind, caliber ML 83 (base caliber Valjoux 23), from 1999

Kelek
Chronograph, steel, automatic, Kelek caliber 2060 (base caliber ETA 2892-A2) from 1999

Kurth
Paris Chronograph, yellow gold, automatic, ETA caliber 7750, from 2006

Krieger
Aficionado Chronoscope, steel, automatic, ETA caliber 7750, from 1999

Maurice Lacroix
Chronograph Réserve de Marche, steel/yellow gold, automatic, caliber ML 30 (base caliber ETA 7750), from 1999

Maurice Lacroix
Croneo, steel, automatic, ETA caliber 7750, from 1999

Maurice Lacroix
Pontos Chronograph, steel, automatic, ML caliber 111 (base caliber ETA 7750), from 2006

A. Lange & Söhne
Datograph, platinum, manual wind, Lange caliber L951.1, from 2006

Maurice Lacroix
Masterpiece Venus, white gold, manual wind, ML caliber 36 (base caliber Venus 175), from 2006

A. Lange & Söhne
Double Split, platinum, manual wind, Lange caliber L001.1, two column wheels for operating rattrapante Flyback function, from 2006

A. Lange & Söhne
1815 Chronograph, white gold, manual wind, Lange caliber L951.0, from 2006

émania
hronograph, steel, manual wind
ith column wheel operation,
om 1940

Limes
Integral Chrono, steel, automatic,
ETA caliber 7750, from 2006

Locman
Panorama, rose gold, automatic,
ETA caliber 2894-2, from 2006

Longines
Chronograph, steel, manual wind,
caliber 13ZN, from 1944

emain where they are until the pusher at the
our o'clock position is pressed, at which point
ll of the chronograph hands return to zero.

he split-second hand

here is no other kind of watch that bears as
nany different names for the pièce de résistance
of chronograph design: It's called a rattrapante,
. split-second chronograph, or simply a double-
aanded chronograph. The "double" refers to the
hronograph's central second hands. During
normal chronograph operation, both second
ands run exactly on top of each other, so that
t first glance they appear to be just one hand.

The technical ingenuity of this design rests in the
way that one of the hands can be stopped
ndependently of the other and then catch
ts twin up with one jump. The translation
or "catch up" in French is *rattraper*. So this
stopwatch function is generally termed
'rattrapante." Sometimes the term "double
chronograph" is used, though this is not quite as

Longines
Chronograph, nickel, manual
wind with column wheel
operation, from 1925

Longines
Lindbergh Spirit Chronograph,
steel/yellow gold, bidirectional
rotating bezel for measuring degree
of longitude, automatic, Longines
caliber L674.8 (base caliber
ETA 7750), from 1999

107

Longines
Avigation Chronograph, steel,
automatic, Longines caliber L651
(base caliber ETA 2894-2), from 1999

Longines
Francillon Split-Second Chronograph,
yellow gold, automatic, Longines caliber
L668.2 (base caliber ETA 7750),
from 1999

Longines
Francillon Chronograph, steel,
automatic, Longines caliber L667
(base caliber ETA 7750), from 1999

Longines
Master Collection Chronograph,
steel, automatic, Longines
caliber L651 (base caliber
ETA 2894-2), special edition
Olympia, from 2006

accurate a description; a more common name is a "split-second chronograph"; it is also occasionally described as a "tow-hand."

This name refers to the fact that the "tow-hand" is normally dragged along—towed—around the dial by its twin brother. The particular feature of these watches is the third push-piece that is generally located on the left-hand side of the case or in the winding crown. Its sole purpose is to stop or release the second chronograph hand.

In contrast to their operation, the use of these watches can be quickly explained: Take, for instance, two athletes competing over a set distance. To record the different times for the runners you would normally need two stopwatches—or alternatively one chronograph with a tow-hand. The chronograph has the further benefit that the race results cannot be fudged by pushing one start button after the other. When the starting signal is given, the

Longines
Master Collection Chronograph, steel, automatic, Longines caliber L651 (base caliber ETA 2894-2), from 2006

Minerva
Heritage, steel, manual wind, caliber Venus 175, from 1999

Minerva
Chronograph Antimagnetic, yellow gold, manual wind with column wheel operation, from 1940

Longines
Tonneau Chronograph, steel, automatic, Longines caliber L667 (base caliber ETA 7750), from 1999

Mido
All Dial Chrono Chronometer, steel, automatic, Mido caliber 1320 (base caliber ETA 7750), from 2006

Minerva
Chronograph Athena II, sterling silver, automatic, ETA caliber 7750, from 1999

Montblanc
Masterpiece Chronograph, yellow gold, automatic, ETA 7750, from 1999

Movado
Chronograph, steel, manual wind, caliber Movado C 95M, full calendar with moon phase display, from 1950

Movado
Datron HS360, steel, automatic, caliber 3019PHC (base caliber Zenith 400 El Primero), from 1975

Minerva
Palladio Nostalgia, steel, automatic, ETA caliber 7750, from 1999

Mühle Glashütte
Teutonia II Chronograph, steel, automatic, ETA caliber 7750, from 2006

Franck Muller
Conquistador Chronograph, red gold, automatic, Franck Muller caliber 1185 (base caliber Frédéric Piguet 11.85), from 1999

Franck Muller
Cintrée Curvex Casablanca Chronograph, steel, automatic, FM caliber 7002 CO (base caliber ETA 7750), from 2006

Franck Muller
Cintrée Curvex Chronograph Havana, yellow gold, automatic, Franck Muller caliber 1185 (base caliber Frédéric Piguet 11.85), from 1999

Franck Muller
Master City, red gold, automatic, Franck Muller caliber 7000 (base caliber ETA 7750), from 1999

Franck Muller
Cintrée Curvex Chronograph Birétrograde, white gold, automatic, FM caliber 7000 B, from 2006

Omega
Speedmaster Broad Arrow, steel, automatic, Omega caliber 3303, C.O.S.C. certified chronometer, from 2006

Omega
De Ville Co-Axial Chronograph Rattrapante, steel, automatic, Omega caliber 3612 (base caliber 3303), C.O.S.C. certified chronometer, from 2006

Nivrel
Chronograph Large Minute Hand, steel, automatic, ETA caliber 2892-2 with Dubois-Dépraz chronograph module 2073, from 1999

Omega
Chronograph, steel, manual wind, caliber 33.3 CHRO T6, with column wheel operation, from 1938

Omega
Chronograph, yellow gold, manual wind, caliber 28.1 CHRO T1, one-pusher chronograph with column wheel operation, from 1939

Omega
Speedmaster Professional Mark II, steel, manual wind, caliber 861, from 1968

Omega
Seamaster Professional Chrono Diver, titanium/tantalum/red gold, unidirectional rotating bezel with dive scale, automatic, Omega caliber 1164 (base caliber ETA 7750), C.O.S.C. certified chronometer, from 1999

Omega
Speedmaster Professional, steel,
manual wind, Omega caliber 1863
(base caliber Lémania 1873),
from 1999

Omega De Ville Co-Axial Chronograph Rattrapante, from 2006

Omega
Speedmaster Day-Date, steel,
automatic, Omega caliber 1151 (base
caliber ETA 7751), from 1999

chronograph button at the two o'clock position on the watchcase is pushed, and both athletes and hands set off. When the first runner crosses the finish line, the rattrapante push-piece in the crown or left-hand side of the case is pressed and the tow-hand stops. When the second runner crosses the finish line the chronograph is stopped in the usual manner, the sweep hand also stops and the times of both runners can be read off.

Repeated pressing of the rattrapante push-piece enables successive intervals to be timed. For example, if one wished to measure a longer run

Omega
Dynamic Chrono, steel, automatic, Omega caliber 1138 (base caliber ETA 2890-02), from 1999

Oris
Williams F1 Chronograph, black/PVD-coated stainless steel, automatic, Oris caliber 673 (base caliber ETA 7750), from 2006

Patek Philippe
Eternal Calendar Chronograph, platinum, manual wind, Patek Philippe caliber CH 27-70, from 1999

Panerai
Luminor 1950 Rattrapante, steel, automatic, Panerai caliber OP XVIII, C.O.S.C. certified chronometer, from 2006

with short breaks, the tow-hand would be stopped several times and read off, and when the push-piece was pressed again, the tow-hand would catch up with the principal chronograph hand.

Oris
Big Crown Chronograph, Oris caliber 674 (base caliber ETA 2824-2), from 1999

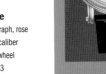

Patek Philippe
Waterproof Chronograph, rose gold, manual wind, caliber 13-30 with column wheel operation, from 1953

Paul Picot
Atelier Split-Second Chronograph, platinum, manual wind, Paul Picot caliber PP310 (base caliber Venus 179), from 1999

Paul Picot
Firshire Tonneau Chronograph, stainless steel, manual wind, ETA caliber 2892-2, from 1999

Péquignet
Mooréa Chronograph Tonneau, stainless steel/yellow gold, automatic, ETA caliber 2894, from 1999

Péquignet
Mooréa Chronograph, stainless steel/yellow gold, automatic, ETA caliber 2824-2 with Dubois-Dépraz chronograph module, C.O.S.C. certified chronometer, from 1999

Paul Picot
Le Chronograph Mythique, stainless
steel/yellow gold, automatic,
modified ETA caliber 7750,
from 1999

Porsche Design
P 6613 PGR, rose gold, automatic,
ETA caliber 7750 AR2, from 2006

Hollow arbors for the hands and the heart piece is back again

In the rattrapante mechanism, the first
chronograph center wheel arbor rotates inside
the hollow minute wheel arbor, and the arbor of
the second chronograph center wheel (split-
seconds wheel) rotates in the arbor of the
principal seconds wheel, which is likewise a
hollow tube.

During normal chronograph operation, a heart-
shaped cam that sits on the chronograph wheel
carries along the split-seconds wheel. A tiny
sprung lever (split-seconds lever) presses against
this cam. On the end of the lever is a tiny cog
that sits between the flats of the heart.
Meanwhile, the two second hands are sitting
exactly on top of one another and when the start
push-piece is pressed, they set off together.

Porsche Design
P 6612 PAC, aluminum/black PVD-
coating, automatic, ETA caliber
2894-2, from 2006

Paul Picot
Technograph, stainless steel,
automatic, ETA caliber 7750,
from 2006

Auguste Reymond
Cotton Club Black Chrono, stainless steel, automatic, ETA caliber 7750, from 1999

Auguste Reymond
Jazz Age, yellow gold, automatic, ETA caliber 7751, moon phase display, from 2006

Porsche Design
Indicator, Titan, automatic, Porsche Design caliber (base caliber ETA 7750), elapsed minutes and seconds are displayed digitally, from 2006

Robergé
Andromède II Chronograph, stainless steel, quartz with mechanical chronograph module, base caliber Frédéric Piguet 1270, from 1999

Robergé
Andromède RS Chronograph, stainless steel, quartz with mechanical chronograph module, base caliber Frédéric Piguet 1270, from 1999

Rolex
Oyster Cosmograph Daytona, stainless steel, manual wind, caliber 727, from 1979

Robergé
M31 Chronograph, yellow gold, quartz with mechanical chronograph module, base caliber Frédéric Piguet 1270, from 1999

If the push-piece for the split-second hand is pressed, pincers reminiscent of those of a beetle grab the toothless rattrapante wheel and grip it firmly. The chronograph center wheel continues to run, while the coil is gently pressed against the heart-shaped cam by the spring-powered lever.

If the rattrapante push-piece is pressed again, the sprung lever presses on the lowest point of the cam, between the two flats of the heart, and the rattrapante wheel is instantly returned to its original position and brought into renewed synchronicity with the principal chronograph hand.

Rolex
Oyster Chronograph Antimagnetic Jean-Claude Killy, stainless steel, manual wind, caliber 72C, full calendar, from 1954

Rolex

Oyster Chronograph "Pre-Daytona," stainless steel, manual wind, caliber 722.1, from 1966

Rolex

Oyster Chronographs, all stainless steel and with manual wind mechanisms, left and right caliber R23, center chronograph with full calendar, caliber Valjoux 72 C, from 1945 to 1950

Rolex

Oyster Perpetual Cosmograph Daytona, stainless steel/yellow gold, automatic, Rolex caliber 4130, from 2006

Daniel Roth

Manual wind Chronograph, white gold, base caliber Lémania NL 2310, reworked by Daniel Roth, from 1999

119

Daniel Roth
Automatic Chronograph, stainless steel, base caliber Zenith 400 El Primero, reworked by Daniel Roth, from 1999

Jörg Schauer
Quarada, stainless steel, automatic, ETA caliber 7750, from 2006

Jörg Schauer
Chronograph Kulisse Edition I, stainless steel, automatic, ETA caliber 7750, reworked by Jörg Schauer, from 1999

Scalfaro
Cap Ferrat Chrono Large Date Flyback, stainless steel, automatic, ADK caliber 151 (base caliber ETA 7750), bidirectional rotating inner bezel, from 2006

Jörg Schauer
Chronograph Kulisse Edition 4, stainless steel, automatic, ETA caliber 7750 with design for 24-hour display, reworked by Jörg Schauer, from 1999

Jörg Schauer
Chronograph Kulisse Edition 5, stainless steel, automatic, ETA caliber 7750 with split-second design, reworked by Jörg Schauer, from 1999

Scalfaro

Porto Cervo Chronograph TriCompax, stainless steel, automatic, ADK caliber 150 (base caliber ETA 7750), from 2006

Otto Schlund

Classic Chronograph, stainless steel, automatic, ETA caliber 7750, from 2006

Alexander Shorokhoff

Leo Tolstoi, stainless steel, manual wind, Poljot caliber 3133, from 2006

Schwarz Etienne

Flyback, stainless steel, automatic, LIP caliber 8151 (base caliber ETA 7750), from 2006

Alain Silberstein

Krono A, stainless steel, automatic, Frédéric Piguet caliber 1185, reworked by Alain Silberstein, from 1999

Alain Silberstein
Krono B, stainless steel, automatic,
Lémania caliber 5100, reworked by
Alain Silberstein, from 1999

Alain Silberstein
Bolido Krono Carbonfiber, stainless steel, automatic, Frédéric
Piguet caliber 1185, reworked by Alain Silberstein, from 2006

Sinn
Gold Chronograph, yellow gold, automatic, ETA caliber 7750,
C.O.S.C. certified chronometer, from 1999

Alain Silberstein
Krono Bauhaus 2 Woodland,
stainless steel/Cloisonné-lacquered,
automatic, ETA caliber 7751,
from 1999

Sinn
303 Kristall Yukon Quest
Chronograph, stainless steel,
dehumidifying capsule
screwed into case, cold-
resistant special oil,
automatic, ETA caliber 7750,
from 1999

Sinn
Navigation chronograph, stainless steel/gold-plated,
manual wind, Lémania caliber 1873, from 1999

Sinn
The classic/sporty Chronograph, stainless steel/gold-plated, automatic, ETA caliber 7751, full calendar, moon phase display and 24-hour display, from 1999

Sinn
Multifunction Chronograph, stainless steel, automatic, ETA caliber 7750, 24-hour display (dual time zone), from 2006

Sinn
Rallye Chronograph, stainless steel, automatic, ETA caliber 7750, with power reserve display, from 2006

Flyback

Flyback is the name of another, unusual additional function that has led to renewed interest within the watch industry recently. The expression has nothing to do with flying, but relates to a mechanism whereby the chronograph can be switched back to zero without having to be stopped first.

To achieve this, the chronograph has to be designed in such a way that the reset-to-zero lever, activated by the lower pusher at four o'clock, which is normally blocked when the chronograph function is in operation, can also be moved when the chronograph is running.

When this happens, the lever flips against both heart pieces on the arbors of the chronograph center wheel and the minutes counting wheel. This impact causes the heart pieces to lie flat against the heart piece lever. When the pusher is released, the heart piece lever jumps back and the chronograph immediately runs again.

Countless variations

Describing the variety of wonderful watches classified as chronographs would go far beyond the space available in this book. It is hardly surprising that there are books that deal exclusively with this kind of watch. Their importance is demonstrated by the fact that this

Sothis
Chronograph Spirit of Moon, stainless steel, automatic, ETA caliber 7751, full calendar, from 1999

Sothis
Janus, stainless steel, automatic,
ETA caliber 7750, from 2006

Sothis
Chronograph Big Bridge, stainless
steel, automatic, ETA caliber 2892-A2
with Dubois-Dépraz chronograph
module 2025, from 1999

TAG Heuer
S/el Chronograph, stainless steel,
automatic, ETA caliber 7750,
from 1999

TAG Heuer
6000 Chronometer Chronograph, stainless steel, automatic,
ETA caliber 2894-2, C.O.S.C. certified chronometer, from 1999

TAG Heuer
Monaco Re-Edition, stainless steel, automatic,
ETA caliber 2894-2, from 1999

124

TAG Heuer
Microtimer, stainless steel, quartz, TAG
Heuer caliber HR 03, measuring accuracy
1/1000 seconds, from 2006

TAG Heuer
1964 Heuer Carrera Re-Edition,
stainless steel, manual wind,
Lémania caliber 1873, from 1999

TAG Heuer
Carrera Chronograph, stainless steel,
automatic, TAG Heuer caliber 16
(base caliber ETA 7750), from 2006

chapter takes up almost a fifth of the whole
book. Even more, in fact, since several of the
following chapters (aviator watches, divers'
watches, and calendar watches) are concerned
with timepieces that can also be used for
measuring short intervals of time.

What is particularly gratifying is that over the
last few years several noteworthy new designs
have joined the many ETA/Valjoux Caliber 7750-
based chronographs. Some designs use, among
others, Zenith, Patek Philippe, Rolex, A. Lange &
Söhne, Glashütte Original and Jaeger-LeCoultre
movements. It is also interesting to note that
several watch brands have recently modified the
description "chronograph" for their watches.
With Glashütte Original's "PanoRetroGraph" or
A. Lange & Söhne's "Dato-Graph," new words
have been coined that are as unusual as the
watches that bear the names. To be honest, few
chronograph wearers really need a watch like

TAG Heuer
Link Chronograph, stainless steel, automatic, TAG
Heuer caliber 16 (base caliber ETA 7750), from 2006

TAG Heuer
Monaco Chronograph Steve
McQueen, stainless steel, automatic,
TAG Heuer caliber 17 (base caliber
ETA 2894-2), from 2006

125

TAG Heuer
Monza Chronograph, stainless steel,
automatic, TAG Heuer caliber 17
(base caliber ETA 2894-2),
from 2006

Temption
Complex Chronograph, stainless steel,
automatic, Temption caliber 17.2 (base
caliber ETA 7751), full calendar, 24-hour
display, from 1999

Temption
Chronograph, stainless steel,
automatic, Temption caliber T17.1
(base caliber ETA 7750), from 1999

Temption
Chronograph Formula, stainless steel,
automatic, Temption caliber T17.1
(base caliber ETA 7750), from 2006

TAG Heuer
Calibre 360, stainless steel,
automatic/manual wind, TAG
Heuer caliber 360, measuring
accuracy 1/100 seconds,
from 2006

this. But they are simply nice toys with a
distinctly masculine aura. And a man will always
welcome more of those.

Historical digression:
What is time measurement, actually?

Of course, the question again arises as to how you
actually set about measuring time; what is the
exact definition of the word "time" itself? Prosaic
science teaches us that "time is the sequence of
events." Granted, but how do you measure the
interval from one "event" to the next?

People have created arbitrary units for all
possible measurements, be they of weight, air
pressure, or temperature. Even the original
meter, introduced in 1795 in France as one ten-
millionth of the distance from the equator to
the North Pole along the Paris Meridian, was, at
the end of the day, arbitrarily determined—it
would have been equally possible to define a
meter as a twenty-millionth of the distance from
the north to the south pole.

But we must remember that with the course of
the stars and the regular, constantly recurring
celestial phenomena, nature has provided us

Temption

Cherubin-R Chronograph Rattrapante, stainless steel, automatic, Temption caliber 19.1 (base caliber ETA caliber 7750), split-second hand function, from 2006

Tissot

Chronograph, stainless steel, manual wind with column wheel operation, from 1950

Tissot

Chrono Valjoux, stainless steel, automatic, ETA caliber 7750, from 2006

Tissot

PRS Chrono Valjoux, stainless steel, automatic, ETA caliber 7750, from 2006

Tudor

Oyster Date Chronograph, stainless steel, manual wind, caliber Valjoux 234, from 1980

127

Tudor
Prince Date Chronograph, stainless steel, automatic, ETA caliber 7750-1, from 2006

Tutima
Chronograph F2 PR, stainless steel, automatic, ETA caliber 7750, with power reserve display, from 2006

Ulysse Nardin
Chronograph, yellow gold, manual wind, single pusher chronograph with column wheel, from 1925

Ulysse Nardin
Chronograph, yellow gold, manual wind, one-pusher chronograph with column wheel operation, enamel dial with double tachymeter scale, from 1930

with ideal units for measuring time. For example, the earth's rotation, the phases of the moon or the even rotation of the moon around the earth, the orbit of the sun and the regular appearance of the fixed stars in the night sky were the first observed and "measured" periods of time.

Buildings from antiquity and structures that pre-date our written history bear witness to the extensive knowledge that our ancestors had already gleaned merely from observing the stars. These people were already aware of the return of particular constellations and even decided on specific details of buildings to make them into astronomical instruments. For example, the sun might only shine through a hole in a wall onto a particular point inside a building on the first day of spring and fall.

Even the Catholic church, which had for a long time challenged the existence of our heliocentric planetary system (and wasn't particularly astronomy-friendly, having only vindicated the great astronomer Galileo Galilei

Ulysse Nardin
Marine Chronograph, stainless steel, automatic, Ulysse Nardin caliber 36 (base caliber ETA 2892), from 1999

Right: Three fine chronographs from the traditional Swiss brands Omega, Eterna and IWC

128

Ulysse Nardin
Split-Second Chronograph Berlin I,
yellow gold, automatic, Ulysse Nardin
caliber UN 57, from 1999

Union
Tradition Automatic Chronograph,
stainless steel, automatic, Union
caliber 26-31, from 1999

Union
Sport Chronograph, stainless steel,
automatic, Union caliber 26-31, from 1999

Union
Diplomat Chronograph, stainless steel,
automatic, Union caliber 26-32, from 2006

towards the end of the twentieth century), has admitted that small holes used to be made in the roofs of some churches in Italy. Through these, on particular days of the year—for example, the equinox—a shaft of light fell onto a particular point on the church floor. Some of these light passages were even designed so that over the course of the year, the sunlight, which was concentrated into a point, formed an imaginary line of light on the floor of the church.

Of course, it was to be a long journey from these astronomical observations to accurate time measurement. Ultimately, it came about that the period of time between the highest point of the sun on two successive days was divided into two lots of 12, and the highest point of the sun was then designated the middle of the day—the end of one 12-hour period and the beginning of another.

Union
Tradition Chronograph, stainless steel, automatic, Union caliber 26-31, from 1999

Universal Genève
Chronograph, red gold, manual wind, caliber 285 with column wheel operation, from 1950

Universal Genève
Golden Master Tech, yellow gold, manual wind, Universal Genève caliber 88 (base caliber ETA 7760), from 1999

Universal Genève
Golden Compax 1950, stainless steel, manual wind, Universal Genève caliber 84 (base caliber Lémania 1873), from 1999

Universal Genève
Senna Watch, stainless steel/carbon, manual wind, Universal Genève caliber 98 (base caliber ETA 7750), from 1999

Urban Jürgensen & Sønner
Referenz 1, platinum, automatic,
Zenith caliber 4001 El Primero,
from 2006

Vacheron Constantin
Les Historiques Chronograph, Vacheron
Constantine caliber 1140, from 1999

Vacheron Constantin
Royal Eagle Chronograph, rose gold,
automatic, Vacheron Constantin caliber
1137, from 2006

Vacheron Constantin
Chronograph, yellow gold, manual
wind, caliber V434 with column wheel
operation, from 1938

Victorinox
AirBoss Mach 6, stainless steel,
automatic, ETA caliber 7753, from 2006

132

George J. von Burg
Classic Collection, gold-plated steel,
automatic, ETA 7750, from 2006

Louis Vuitton
Speedy Chronograph Automatique,
steel, automatic, ETA caliber 2894-2,
from 2006

Raymond Weil
Parsifal Chronograph, steel/yellow-
gold, automatic, ETA caliber 2829-A2,
from 1999

The resulting hours—which the Catholic-influenced Romance languages called *hora*, *heures*, or *ora* after the prayer said at canonical hours—were in turn divided into 60 smaller periods of time, the minutes (from Latin *minuere*, meaning "to diminish"). The second subdivision of the hour (Latin *secunda*, meaning "second") into even smaller segments, introduced later, was in turn one sixtieth of the minute, so stayed within the twelve-fold system.

In English, this division of the day into two lots of 12 hours became particularly embedded in the language, because "forenoon" (from 12:00 midnight) is generally denoted with "ante

meridian" (a.m—*ante* being the Latin for "before"), and "afternoon" (from midday to midnight) with "post meridian" (p.m—*post* being the Latin for "after"), which only reifies the climb of the sun to its highest point on the meridian as it stands vertical to the horizon, and its subsequent descent.

Because of the tilting of the earth's axis, this climb and descent takes place in daylight periods of varying length in summer and winter, resulting in hours during the Middle Ages also being of an irregular length. This came to an end after the invention of the first gear clocks, because a clockwork movement runs down at an

Raymond Weil
Parsifal Chronograph, stainless steel, automatic, RW caliber 7300 (base caliber ETA 2894-2), from 2006

Raymond Weil
Saxo Automatic Chronograph, stainless steel, automatic, ETA caliber 7750, from 1999

Xemex
Avenue Chronograph, stainless steel, automatic ETA 2894-2, from 2006

even rate influenced to a limited extent by the regulation of an oscillating system (verge-and-foliot, balance, pendulum).

When the measurement of time wasn't taken quite so seriously, clocks only had one hand, for the hours. Accuracy of the measurement process, vaguely comparable to the precision of mechanical clocks by today's standards, was only reached during the eighteenth century.

Zenith
Grand ChronoMaster GT, stainless steel, automatic, Zenith caliber 4001 El Primero, from 2006

Harry Winston
Pulsometer Chronograph, platinum, automatic Frédéric Piguet caliber 1185, from 1999

Zenith
Class El Primero, stainless steel, automatic, Zenith caliber 4002 El Primero, from 2006

Zenith

Chronomaster Chronograph,
stainless steel, automatic, Zenith
caliber 400 El Primero, C.O.S.C.
certified chronometer, from 1999

Zenith

Class 4 Chronograph, stainless
steel, automatic, Zenith caliber 400
El Primero, from 1999

Zenith

Chronograph, sterling silver, manual
wind, crown pusher chronograph with
column wheel operation, from 1920

Zenith

Port-Royal Open Concept, titanium,
automatic, Zenith caliber 4021 C El Primero,
works partly skeletonized from 2006

Zenith

Chronomaster Open XXT, stainless
steel, automatic, Zenith caliber 4021
El Primero, works partly skeletonized,
from 2006

Zenith

Rainbow Chronograph, steel, automatic, Zenith
caliber 400 El Primero, from 1999

3. AVIATOR WATCHES

What *is* a proper aviator watch? This is a subject discussed as frequently, and often as hotly, by pilots as by watch manufacturers. The smallest common denominator is generally that an aviator watch must be a highly accurate timekeeper that can be read easily, even in unfavorable conditions. At the same time there is a whole range of features that are definitely as important in the cockpit as they are in everyday life.

Aristo
XL Edition Navigator, stainless steel, automatic, ETA caliber 2801, from 2006

Bell & Ross
Instrument BR01-94, stainless steel/black PVD-coated, automatic, ETA caliber 2894-2, chronograph, from 2006

Bell & Ross
Vintage 126 XL, stainless steel, automatic, ETA caliber 2894-2, chronograph, from 2006

The jewelry and watch manufacturer Cartier is not necessarily regarded as a sports watch specialist. And yet the first timepiece to have earned the designation "aviator watch" came from this very company. During a dinner in Maxim's, Alberto Santos-Dumont, renowned in Parisian society as a dandy and an aviation pioneer during the Belle Époque, was explaining the big problem with his pocket watch. Because he had his hands literally full when carrying out his experiments with helium balloons, he simply wasn't able to monitor his flight times.

This was the era when pocket watches were carried on gold chains. To pull it out of his pocket, read it, and put it back in the pocket would have entailed an extremely dangerous loss of control over the aircraft. Louis-Joseph Cartier, a friend of Santos-Dumont, was listening attentively—and together with the watchmaker and master craftsman, Edmond Jaeger, he developed the first wristwatch. It had Roman numerals, two hands, a crown with a good grip, and it was fastened to the wearer's wrist by means of a leather strap.

Good legibility is the number one priority

This historical retrospective highlights features that are still important. These include, first and

Breitling
Navitimer, stainless steel, manual
wind, Venus caliber 178,
chronograph, bidirectional rotating
bezel with slide rule scale, from 1969

Breguet
Transatlantique, stainless steel, automatic,
Breguet caliber 582Q, chronograph with Flyback
function, bidirectional rotating bezel, from 1999

Breitling
Colt Ocean Automatic, stainless steel, automatic,
Breitling caliber 17 (base caliber ETA 2892-2),
unidirectional 60-minute bezel, from 1999

Breguet
Type XX Transatlantique, stainless
steel, automatic, Breguet caliber
582Q, chronograph with Flyback
function, bidirectional rotating
bezel, from 2006

Breitling
Navitimer, stainless steel, automatic,
caliber 12 with micro motor,
chronograph, bidirectional rotating
bezel with slide rule scale, from 1968

139

Breitling

Colt Superocean, yellow gold, automatic, Breitling caliber 10 (base caliber ETA 2892-2), C.O.S.C. certified chronometer, unidirectional 60-minute bezel, from 1969

Breitling

Spatiographe, stainless steel, automatic, Breitling caliber 36 (base caliber ETA 2892-A2), ten-minute digital totalizer at nine o'clock, bidirectional rotating bezel with slide rule scale, from 2006

Breitling

Montbrillant, stainless steel, automatic, Breitling caliber 19 (base caliber ETA 2892-A2), full calendar with moon phase display, bidirectional rotating bezel with slide rule scale, from 1999

Breitling

Navitimer Twinsixty, stainless steel, automatic, Breitling caliber 36 (base caliber ETA 2892-A2), bidirectional rotating bezel with slide rule scale, from 1999

Breitling
Navitimer Heritage, white gold, automatic, Breitling caliber 35 (base caliber ETA 2892-2), C.O.S.C. certified chronometer, bidirectional rotating bezel with slide rule scale, from 2006

Breitling
Emergency Mission, stainless steel, quartz, Breitling caliber 73 (base caliber ETA 251.262), C.O.S.C. certified chronometer, bidirectional 60-minute bezel, distress transmitter, from 2006

foremost, secure attachment of the watch to the wrist, and in such a way that it can always be seen and read. Pilots in the First and Second World Wars sometimes had their watches fitted with extra-long leather straps that allowed the watch to be worn over a thick jacket or overalls—if necessary even on the thigh.

The second important feature of an aviator watch is its instant legibility. This is an area where, even in the digital age, an analog watch scores over a digital. We Westerners are so used to them that we are able to interpret the position of two hands in a fraction of a second, whereas a digital display has to be read properly. This is also an important consideration for the armed forces. Easy readability is the number one priority. It is for this reason that most modern timepieces that are designated "aviator watches" have black dials with white numbers and hands, which also have a luminous coating and a specially marked 12 o'clock position for better night-time visibility. This was how the first "Special Watch for Pilots" made by Swiss manufacturer IWC looked; which also featured

Certina
DS Pilot Automatic Chrono, stainless steel, automatic, Certina caliber 674 (base caliber ETA 7750), from 2006

Breitling
Navitimer, stainless steel, automatic, Breitling caliber 23 (base caliber ETA 7750), C.O.S.C. certified chronometer, bidirectional rotating bezel with slide rule scale, from 2006

Cyma

Military watch, manual wind, stainless steel, British military wristwatch, from 1940

Doxa

Flieger II, stainless steel, manual wind, ETA caliber 2801, from 2006

Doxa

Aviator Chronograph, stainless steel, manual wind, German Luftwaffe military watch, from 1940

Chronoswiss

Timemaster Flyback, stainless steel, automatic, Chronoswiss caliber C.673 (base caliber ETA 7750), chronograph with Flyback function, dial with luminescent coating, from 2006

Doxa

Antimagnetic, stainless steel, manual wind, from 1940

Enicar
Jet Graph, stainless steel, manual wind, caliber Valjoux 724, rotating bezel for setting a second time zone, from 1969

Eterna
Airforce III Chronograph, stainless steel, automatic, ETA caliber 7750, bidirectional 60-minute bezel, from 1999

Eterna
Airforce II, stainless steel, automatic, ETA caliber 2824-2, from 1999

Eterna
Aviator Watch, stainless steel, manual wind, caliber 852S, German Luftwaffe military watch, from 1935

143

Excelsior Park
Chronograph Monte Carlo, stainless steel, manual wind, caliber Valjoux 7740, rotating 60-minute bezel, from 1975

Fortis
Automatic Aviator Chronograph, stainless steel, automatic, ETA caliber 7750, from 1999

Fortis
Pilot Professional Automatic, steel/black PVD-coated, automatic, ETA caliber 2836-2, from 1999

a rotating glass bezel with a luminous arrow index.

A prime example with regard to ease of legibility is deemed to be the *Beobachtungsuhr*—or "B-Uhr" for short—used by German Luftwaffe pilots. They were made in the 1940s by Wempe, Lange & Söhne, and IWC, as well as the Pforzheim brands Stowa and Laco. Today the ranges of the last three brands feature modern versions of their earlier *Profiuhren*, which are very popular with the public, mainly due to their functionality, but also because of their history.

Soft iron inner cases give protection from magnetic fields

Strictly speaking, magnetic field protection for the movement has been one of the key features of watches since the Second World War. The screens of the ground-penetrating radars,

Jacques Etoile
Lissabon Grand Aviator, stainless steel, manual wind, modified ETA caliber Unitas, from 1999

Fortis
B-42 Official Cosmonaut's Chronograph, stainless steel, automatic ETA caliber 7750, special edition with engraving on case back (picture of ISS space station), limited to 500 copies, from 2006

Fortis
Official Cosmonaut's Chronograph, stainless steel, automatic, Lémania caliber 5100, additional 24-hour display (second time zone), from 1999

Fortis
Automatic Aviator, stainless steel, automatic, ETA caliber 2824-2, from 2006

Glashütte Original
Senator Aviator Automatic Panorama Date, stainless steel, automatic, Glashütte Original caliber 39-42, from 1999

Glashütter Uhrenbetrieb
Tutima Chronograph, stainless steel, manual wind, Urofa caliber 59 with column wheel operation, known as the Wehrmachtschronograph (army chronograph), from 1942

Glashütte Original
Senator Aviator Automatic, stainless steel, automatic, Glashütte Original caliber 39-10, from 1999

Glashütte Original
Senator Aviator Chronograph, stainless steel, automatic, Glashütte Original caliber 39-30, from 1999

installed in increasing numbers, generated magnetic fields of such intensity that a watch's operation could be considerably influenced.

Nowadays alloys are used in the escapement mechanism, particularly for the hairspring, because they are less sensitive towards magnetism. However, magnetic fields in cockpits can still have a negative influence on a watch. Even today, aviator watch manufacturers such as Sinn and IWC, who follow accepted wisdom, continue to equip their timepieces with inner casings made from soft iron that leads the magnetic fields around the movement.

For pilots and "seconds pinchers" amongst watch-lovers, a watch without a stop-seconds function is inconceivable. This is a mechanism that stops the watch when the crown is pulled out and starts it again when it is pushed in. This allows watches to be synchronized with each other or with an external radio signal, something that is particularly valuable when used by the military.

Hamilton
Aviator Watch, stainless steel, manual wind, caliber H75, British Royal Air Force military watch, from 1965

Glycine
Airman MLV, stainless steel, automatic, ETA caliber 2893-2, additional 24-hour display (second time zone), dial fully luminescent-coated, from 2006

Hamilton

Military Watch, manual wind, caliber H75, British military watch, from 1973

Hanhart

Tachy-Tele, stainless steel, manual wind, Hanhart caliber 40, German military chronograph with tachymeter and telemeter scales, from 1935

Hanhart

One-Touch Aviator Chronograph, stainless steel, manual wind, Hanhart caliber 40, German Luftwaffe military watch, from 1935

Hamilton

Aviator Chronograph, stainless steel, manual wind, caliber Valjoux 7733, British Royal Air Force military watch, from 1969

Hanhart

One-Touch Aviator Chronograph, stainless steel, manual wind, Hanhart caliber 40, bidirectional rotating bezel with reference mark, German Luftwaffe military watch, from 1936

Hanhart

Aviator Chronograph, stainless steel, manual wind, Hanhart caliber 40, bidirectional rotating bezel with reference mark, German Luftwaffe military watch, from 1945

147

Heuer

German Army Aviator Chronograph, stainless steel, manual wind, caliber Valjoux 233, chronograph with Flyback function, bidirectional rotating bezel with 0 to 60 markings, from 1970

Hanhart

Tachy-Tele Replica, stainless steel, manual wind, ETA caliber 7760, chronograph, bidirectional rotating bezel with reference markings, from 2006

Hanhart

Primus, stainless steel, manual wind, Hanhart caliber 704 (base caliber ETA 7760), single-pusher chronograph, bidirectional rotating bezel with reference markings, from 2006

Hanhart

Pioneer Caliber II, stainless steel, automatic, Hanhart caliber 716 (base caliber ETA 7750), chronograph, bidirectional rotating bezel with luminous mark, from 2006

Heuer

Aviator Chronograph, stainless steel, manual wind, caliber Valjoux 7733, chronograph with Flyback function, bidirectional rotating bezel with 0 to 12 markings, Argentine Air Force military watch, from 1975

IWC

Mark XI, stainless steel, automatic, IWC caliber 89, soft iron inner case for protection against magnetic fields, British Royal Air Force military watch, from 1951

Ikepod

Megapode Pilot Chronograph, stainless steel, automatic, ETA caliber 7750, C.O.S.C. certified chronometer, additional 24-hour display (second time zone), rotating bezel under glass with slide rule function, from 1999

IWC

Aviator Watch, stainless steel, manual wind, IWC caliber 52, German Luftwaffe military watch, from 1940

IWC

Mark X, stainless steel, automatic, IWC caliber 83, soft iron inner case for protection against magnetic fields, British Royal Air Force military watch, from 1944

IWC

Mark XII, stainless steel, automatic, IWC caliber C.884/2, soft iron inner case for protection against magnetic fields, from 1999

149

IWC

Mark XV, stainless steel,
automatic, IWC caliber 37524
(base caliber ETA 2892-A2),
soft iron inner case for
protection against magnetic
fields, from 2006

Robust construction is a necessity

Although it is generally dry in cockpits—the one
exception being pre-war aircraft—even a pilot's
watch comes into contact with water time and
again both before and after the flight, making
water-resistance another essential feature. But a
word of caution: Don't trust everything you read
on a watch! A watch declared water-resistant to
a depth of 98 feet (30 meters) in accordance with
DIN specifications is not suitable for anything
like a dive to 98 feet. Watches like this are
immune to spray, hand washing or a walk in
the rain, but if you want to go for a swim with
your watch, select one that is water-resistant
to 328 feet (100 meters), according to DIN
specifications.

IWC

UTC, stainless steel, automatic, IWC caliber C.37526, additional 24-hour display in dial window at 12 o'clock (second zone time), soft iron inner case for protection against magnetic fields, from 1999

IWC

Aviator chronograph, stainless steel, automatic, IWC caliber C.7922 (base caliber ETA 7750), soft iron inner case for protection against magnetic fields, from 1999

IWC

Aviator Watch Double Chronograph, stainless steel, automatic, IWC caliber 79230 (base caliber ETA 7750), chronograph with split-second hand, soft iron inner case for protection against magnetic fields, from 1999

IWC

Large Aviator Watch, stainless steel, automatic, IWC caliber 5011, soft iron inner case for protection against magnetic fields, from 2006

151

This IWC Double Chrono has classic aviator watch looks: clearly legible dial typography, additional functions and a case in non-reflective matte black

In a pilot's everyday life, the quality of the watch is also of paramount importance. So the Omega Speedmaster Professional, which became known as the "Moon Watch" after being used in various Apollo missions, was and still is fitted with a plastic crystal. Due to its resilience, it can equalize differences in pressure without jumping out or cracking, although it is susceptible to scratching. However, in contrast to mineral glass crystals, scratches can be polished out of Plexiglas. Nowadays, the first choice for quality watches is a sapphire crystal with a non-reflective coating on one side. These watch crystals are scratch-resistant and easy to read.

IWC

Spitfire Double Chronograph, stainless steel, automatic,
IWC caliber 79230 (base caliber ETA 7750),
chronograph with split-second hand, soft iron inner
case for protection against magnetic fields, from 2006

Jaeger-LeCoultre

LeCoultre Chronograph, stainless
steel, manual wind, caliber Valjoux
72, bidirectional rotating bezel with
0 to 60 markings, from 1970

Daniel JeanRichard

Bressel Militaire, stainless steel, manual wind,
caliber 16 DJR (base caliber ETA Unitas), from 1999

Junghans

German Military Aviator Chronograph,
stainless steel/chrome-plated,
manual wind, Junghans caliber 88,
German Luftwaffe military watch,
from 1950

Daniel JeanRichard

Automatic Militaire, stainless steel, automatic,
caliber 24 DJR (base caliber ETA 2824-2), from 1999

Junghans
Military Aviator Chronograph,
stainless steel/chrome-plated,
manual wind, Junghans caliber 88,
bidirectional rotating bezel with 0 to
60 markings, German Luftwaffe
military watch, from 1955

Junghans
Chronograph, stainless steel, manual
wind, Junghans caliber 88, from 1945

The watch as a navigational aid

An important function of the watch in the
pioneer years of flying was navigation,
particularly for long-distance flights. Pilots
navigated in the same way as sailors, and using
the same aids, which included an accurately
functioning watch. Charles A. Lindbergh wore a
watch like this during his first Atlantic crossing.
His annoyance over the shortcoming of this
timepiece enriched the world of watches with
another function: It enabled the geographical
longitude to be calculated using degrees and
minutes of arc.

Lindbergh's friendship with the President of the
Fédération Aéronautique Internationale, John
Heinmüller, whose main profession was
Chairman of Longines Wittnauer Watch Co. in
the USA, was instrumental in the creation of the

Junghans
Pilot Automatic, stainless steel, automatic, ETA caliber 2824-2,
unidirectional rotating bezel with 0 to 60 markings, from 2006

Laco
Automatic Aviator
Chronograph, stainless steel,
automatic, ETA caliber 7750,
from 2006

Laco
Series I Automatic Aviator
Chronograph, stainless steel,
automatic, ETA caliber 2824-2,
from 2006

A. Lange & Söhne
Aviator Watch, silver, manual wind, Lange caliber 45, German Luftwaffe military watch, from 1943

A. Lange & Söhne
B-Uhr Navigation Watch, silver, manual wind, Lange caliber with optimum timekeeping performance, degree measuring watch for the German Luftwaffe, only nine copies of this model were made, from 1939

Lémania
Aviator Chronograph, stainless steel, manual wind, German Luftwaffe military watch, from 1938

155

Lémania
One-Touch Aviator Chronograph, stainless steel, manual wind, Lémania caliber 2220, Swedish Air Force military watch, from 1960

Lémania
Aviator Watch, stainless steel, manual wind, German Luftwaffe military watch, from 1935

Lémania
One-Touch Aviator Chronograph, stainless steel, manual wind, Lémania caliber 2220, British Royal Air Force military watch, from 1965

Lémania
One-Touch Aviator Chronograph, stainless steel, manual wind, Lémania caliber 2225, British Royal Air Force military watch, from 1950

Longines
Weems, stainless steel, manual wind, Longines caliber 12.68N, rotating bezel with 0 to 60 markings, British Royal Air Force navigation watch, from 1938

legendary "Hour Angle Watch." Based on Lindbergh's ideas and sketches, the timepiece was presented in 1931. It had a device for quick alignment of the seconds with a time signal—an inner dial that could be adjusted using the crown. The rotating bezel was divided into 15 degrees (with subdivisions into 15, 30, and 45 minutes of arc), as the earth turns by exactly 15 degrees in one hour (360 degrees in 24 hours = 15 degrees in one hour). Besides the 12-hour scale, the main dial was also subdivided into 180 degrees (corresponding to the earth's rotation in half a day). The rotating sub-dial was printed with 60-degree and 15-degree scales.

All of these scales and data necessitated a large dial so that it was still possible to see the big

Longines
Aviator Watch, stainless steel, manual wind, Longines caliber 15.94, German Luftwaffe military watch, from 1936

Longines

Aviator Watch, stainless steel, manual wind, Longines caliber 330, rotating bezel with 0 to 12 markings, from 1968

Longines

Lindbergh Hour Angle Watch, yellow gold, automatic, Longines caliber L.614.2 (base caliber ETA 2892-A2), bidirectional rotating bezel for calculating longitude, replica of historic Lindbergh watch, from 1999

Longines

Aviator Watch, stainless steel, manual wind, Longines caliber 14.68N, British Air Force military watch, from 1951

Marcello C.

Aviator Chronograph, stainless steel, automatic, ETA caliber 7750, from 1999

Longines

Lindbergh Hour Angle Watch, stainless steel, manual wind, Longines caliber 18.69N, bidirectional rotating bezel for calculating longitude, from 1936

157

Minerva
Aviator Chronograph, stainless steel,
manual wind, German Luftwaffe
military watch with tachymeter scale,
from 1940

Marcello C.
Automatic Aviator, stainless steel,
automatic, ETA caliber 2824-2, from 1999

Minerva
Palladio S Aviation, stainless steel,
automatic, ETA caliber 7750, from 1999

Minerva
Aviator Chronograph, stainless steel,
manual wind, single button
chronograph, from 1930

Minerva
Pythagore Aviation, stainless
steel, automatic, Minerva
caliber 48, from 1999

Nivada
Aviator Sea Diver, stainless steel,
manual wind, caliber Landeron 248,
rotating bezel, from 1969

Mühle Glashütte
Marine Aviation Chronograph III, stainless steel,
automatic, ETA caliber 7750, bidirectional rotating
bezel with 0 to 60 markings, from 1999

Mühle Glashütte
Marine Aviation Chronometer M2, stainless
steel, automatic, ETA caliber 2824-2,
C.O.S.C. certified chronometer, from 1999

Mühle Glashütte
Lufthansa Tachymeter, stainless steel,
automatic, ETA caliber 7750,
bidirectional rotating inner bezel with
0 to 60 markings, from 2006

Mühle Glashütte
Big Sports M12, stainless steel,
automatic, ETA caliber 2824-2, from 2006

Nivrel
Automatic Day Date, stainless steel,
automatic, ETA caliber 2836-2,
from 1999

N. B. Yaeger
Tango, stainless steel, automatic, ETA caliber 2893-2, additional 24-hour display (second time zone), from 2006

N. B. Yaeger
Delta, stainless steel, automatic, ETA caliber 2824-2, from 2006

N. B. Yaeger
Charlie, stainless steel, automatic, ETA caliber 7750, from 2006

Omega
Air Ministry Aviator Watch, stainless steel, manual wind, Omega caliber 23.4SC, rotating bezel with Weems seconds-setting, British Royal Air Force navigation watch, from 1940

Omega
Speedmaster Professional, stainless steel, manual wind, Omega caliber 321, chronograph, from 1963

Omega
Aviator Watch, stainless steel, manual wind, Omega caliber 283, soft iron inner case for protection against magnetic fields, British Royal Air Force military watch, from 1953

picture when faced with this wealth of information. So the finished watch measured 1.9 inches (47.5 millimeters) in diameter. If the time signal was correctly set, the information in the Nautical Almanac taken into consideration, and a sextant used to calculate the degrees of latitude, it really was possible to read off the degree of longitude of one's actual position. Of course nowadays, in our age of radar, GPS, and radio systems, something that was crucially important to Lindbergh and his contemporaries is just history and no longer particularly relevant. Today's pilots have completely different requirements for their watches.

Oris

Flight Timer, stainless steel, automatic, ETA caliber with second zone time (at three o'clock), inner rotating bezel operated by separate crown at two o'clock (third time zone), from 2006

Perrelet

Air Zermatt II, stainless steel, automatic, ETA caliber 2892-A2, inner rotating bezel with 0 to 60 markings, operated with additional crown at two o'clock, from 1999

Omega

Flightmaster, stainless steel, manual wind, Omega caliber 911, chronograph, second zone time display, inner rotating bezel (Réhau) with 60-minute scale, from 1963

Omega

Speedmaster Moonwatch Replica, stainless steel, manual wind, Omega caliber 1861 (base caliber Lémania 1873), chronograph, from 1999

Poljot

JAK-7, stainless steel, manual wind, Poljot caliber 3133, chronograph, from 2006

Record

Aviator Watch, stainless steel, manual wind, caliber 022K, British military watch, from 1948

Revue Thommen

Airspeed Chronograph II, stainless steel, automatic, ETA caliber 7750, rotating bezel with 60-minute scale, from 1999

Revue Thommen

Airspeed Automatic, stainless steel, automatic, ETA caliber 2836-2, from 1999

Revue Thommen

Airspeed Flyback, stainless steel, automatic, LIP caliber 8151 (base caliber ETA 7750), chronograph with Flyback function, from 2006

Revue Thommen

Airspeed Altimeter, titanium, manual wind, ETA caliber 7001, mechanical altimeter, from 1999

Chronographs are in great demand from modern pilots

One of the most popular features at the moment is the chronograph stop function for measuring short intervals of time (up to 12 hours). Porsche Design's "Indicator" has assumed a special position among modern aviator chronographs. It is the only chronograph that displays stop minutes and hours in a digital readout—purely mechanically, of course.

Advanced aviator watch fans tend to choose rattrapante chronographs with two timing hands. One hand is stopped to determine an intermediate or reference time, while the other hand continues to sweep around, hence the description "split second." If the reference time is no longer required, just one push on the button and the split-second hand jumps to rejoin the regular timing hand. So it catches it up, hence the description "rattrapante," from

Otto Schlund
Korona Sport Aviator, stainless steel, automatic, ETA caliber 2824-2, from 2006

Sinn
Aviator Chronograph, stainless steel, automatic, ETA caliber 7750, chronograph, from 2006

Sinn
Aviator Chronograph, stainless steel, automatic, Lémania caliber 5100, stop-second and central minute timer, 24-hour display, from 1999

Sinn
Aviator Chronograph, stainless steel, automatic, Lémania caliber 5100, stop-second and central minute timer, 24-hour display, from 1999

Sinn
Space Chronograph, stainless steel, automatic, Lémania caliber 5100, stop-second and central minute timer, 24-hour display, from 1999

Sinn
Aviator Watch with magnetic field protection, stainless steel, automatic, ETA caliber 2824-2, soft iron inner case for protection against magnetic fields, from 2006

163

Sinn
Aviator Watch with captive bezel, stainless steel, automatic, ETA caliber 2824-2, soft iron inner case for protection against magnetic fields, from 2006

TAG Heuer
Autavia, stainless steel, automatic TAG Heuer caliber 11 (base caliber Dubois-Dépraz 2022), from 2006

Stowa
Aviator, stainless steel, automatic, ETA caliber 2824, extra long leather strap, from 2006

Tissot

T-Touch Tech, stainless steel, quartz, ETA caliber E40.305, multifunctional electronics module with altimeter, chronograph etc. operated by touch-sensitive sensors in the crystal, from 2006

Tutima

Aviator chronograph 1941, stainless steel, manual wind, ETA caliber 7760, bidirectional rotating bezel with reference marking, from 1999

Tudor

Oyster Prince Ranger, stainless steel, automatic, from 1975

Tutima

Aviator Chronograph F2, stainless steel, automatic, ETA caliber 7750, bidirectional rotating bezel with reference marking, from 1999

Tutima

Military Aviator Chronograph T, titanium, automatic, Lémania caliber 5100, stop-second and central minute timer, 24-hour display, from 1999

Tutima

Pacific, stainless steel, automatic, ETA caliber 2836-2, bidirectional rotating bezel with 60-minute scale, from 1999

165

Tutima
Automatic FX, stainless steel,
automatic, ETA caliber 2836-2, bezel
with 60-minute scale, from 2006

Tutima
Classic Aviator Chronograph,
stainless steel, manual wind,
ETA caliber 7760, bezel with
reference marking, from 2006

Tutima
Military Aviator Chronograph II, stainless
steel, automatic, Lémania caliber 5100,
stop-seconds and central minute timer,
24-hour display, bezel with 60-minute sc
from 2006

Ulysse Nardin
Aviator Chronograph A.R.A.
Navigacion, silver, manual wind,
crown pusher chronograph,
from 1925

the French *rattraper*, meaning "to catch up"
(see "Chronograph" chapter). The Flyback
function is also popular with many pilots.
This enables the chronograph to be reset
to zero and to continue running without
pressing the start/stop button. Thus, with
just one push of a button a new
measurement can be started. Incidentally,
the only chronograph to combine the
rattrapante, Flyback and automatic
movement is the Blancpain Léman
Flyback Split-Second.

Frequent fliers, particularly those who
move between different time zones, tend
to choose watches which can display at
least two times at once (e.g. the time at
home and local time, or Zulu and local
time). However, we have devoted the
chapter "GMT and World Time Watches"

Union
Aviator Chronograph,
stainless steel, automatic
Union caliber 26-32,
from 2006

Union
Aviator Small Second, stainless steel,
automatic Union caliber 26-05,
from 2006

Universal Genève
Rattrapante Aviator Chronograph,
steel, manual wind, 24-hour dial,
from 1940

167

Zenith
Aviator Chronograph, steel,
automatic, Zenith caliber 146 DP,
rotating bezel with 60-minute scale,
from 1970

Victorinox
AirBoss Mach 4 XL de Luxe, steel, manual wind, ETA caliber
6498-2, inner bezel with 60-minute scale, from 2006

Zenith
Rainbow Chronograph Flyback, steel, automatic,
Zenith caliber 400 El Primero, from 1999

Zenith
Aviator Chronograph, steel,
automatic, Zenith caliber 3091PHC,
rotating bezel with 60-minute scale,
approx. 2,700 examples of this watch
were made, from 1972

to these watches. There is also an explanation of
the technical functions of this kind of watch.

While the wristwatch was an essential piece
of aircraft equipment in the early days of
aviation, today it generally has a completely
different function. Sergio de Witt, a Lufthansa
captain on an MD-11 Freighter, philosophized:
"The more digitized and highly technical our
environment becomes, the greater the wish will
be for something tangible and down to earth.
That is embodied in a mechanical watch. It
represents a likeable contrast to our fully
electronic working environment. That is where
I think their charm lies."

The models for today's aviator watches
originated during the Second World War and
were primarily designed for optimum ease of
use. Pictured to the right are two historic IWC
watches from the 1940s.

4. DIVERS' WATCHES

Diving as a sport did not become really popular until about 25 years ago. Divers' watches, however, have been around for over 70 years. Books could be written about the development of divers' watches, chronographs and alarms. We are going to devote one chapter to the topic, turning the spotlight to illuminate individual episodes in the history of the diver's watch.

Bertolucci
Vir Maris men's diving watch, steel, automatic, ETA caliber 2892-A2, C.O.S.C. certified chronometer, water-resistant to 985 feet (300 m), unidirectional rotating diver's bezel, from 1999

Blancpain
Fifty Fathoms diver's watch and diver's chronograph, steel, automatic, Blancpain caliber, water-resistant to 985 feet (300 m), unidirectional rotating diver's bezel, from the 1950s

Blancpain
Fifty Fathoms, steel, automatic, Blancpain caliber 1151, two spring barrels, water-resistant to 985 feet (300 m), unidirectional rotating diver's bezel, from 2006

The year 1927 probably counts as the year of birth of the water-resistant wristwatch. The young sportswoman Mercedes Gleitze swam the English Channel from Calais to Dover with a Rolex on her wrist. Its case structure was patented, and among its distinguishing features was a back with a screw thread that allowed itself to be screwed into the case, plus a screw-threaded crown. The whole was supposed to be as watertight as an oyster, and so it was given its name. The Channel crossing offered the first public demonstration of this feature, and it made the papers on November 24 of that year. "Rolex Oyster, the wonder watch that defies the elements," was the headline on the front page of the *Daily Mail*. This did not happen quite by chance, as Hans Wilsdorf, the owner of Rolex, had bought the front page of the newspaper, which had circulation figures in the millions, for 40,000 Swiss francs.

Blancpain
Air Command Concept, steel/rubber, automatic, Blancpain caliber F185, chronograph, water-resistant 657 feet (200 m), unidirect rotating diver's bezel, from

Certina
DS-3 Super PH 1000 m, steel,
automatic, caliber 919-1,
unidirectional rotating diver's
bezel, water-resistant to 3280 feet
(1000 m), from 1975

Breitling
Chrono Superocean, steel, automatic, Breitling caliber 13
(base ETA 7750), chronograph, C.O.S.C. certified
chronometer, water-resistant to 1640 feet (500 m),
unidirectional rotating diver's bezel, from 2006

Bulgari
Scuba Chrono, steel, automatic, GP caliber 2282,
chronograph, C.O.S.C. certified chronometer,
water-resistant to 657 feet (200 m), unidirectional
rotating diver's bezel, from 1999

Certina
DS-2, steel, automatic, caliber
25-651, unidirectional rotating
diver's bezel, water-resistant to
328 feet (100 m), from 1968

This headline made the brand famous overnight, and ever since then it has been the name synonymous with a sturdy sports watch. Rolex did not become a diver's watch until much later. The Oyster case was systematically improved and was the foundation for the first Submariner, which came onto the market in 1953 and was water-resistant to a depth of 328 feet (100 meters). Only a year later, the water resistance was doubled to 657 feet (200 meters). A not inconsiderable contribution to this development came from two Swiss researchers, Auguste and Jacques Piccard, who went on their expeditions equipped with Rolex watches and gave the manufacturer's research and development staff many useful tips. Jacques Piccard made a spectacular advertisement for Rolex in 1960 by taking an Oyster on his dive into the Mariana Trench. He did not, however, wear it on his wrist. The timepiece was a special design called the Deep Sea

Special Oyster, fixed to the outer shell of the submarine *Trieste*. The timepiece, with its hefty case and hemispherical glass, withstood water pressure of more than six tons per square inch at 38,815 feet (1 tonne per square centimeter at 10,916 meters) and remained absolutely watertight. The mass-produced mechanism fulfilled its task with no problems at all.

Rolex underwater timepieces were around well before Rolex divers' watches. In 1936, the Italian company Guido Panerai & Figlio, which later became Officine Panerai, designed the first prototype of a diver's watch. The client was the Italian navy, which had previously tested various Swiss watches but had not been satisfied. Now it was the turn of the Florentine company, specializing in fine mechanisms, which had also made mechanical depth gauges, compasses and torpedo detonators for the navy.

Chopard

L.U.C. Pro One, steel, automatic, L.U.C. caliber 4/96, C.O.S.C. certified chronometer, water-resistant to 985 feet (300 m), unidirectional rotating diver's bezel, from 2006

Panerai built a Rolex caliber into the case of a modified depth meter and delivered it in the same year to the Admiralty, which then ordered ten of them. The delivery of these watches in 1938 made Panerai the official watch supplier to the Italian navy.

The dial was a special feature. It was distinguished by optimum legibility, even in total darkness, and was comprised of two parts. The upper part was a black disk, with large figures and indexes punched out of it, and the lower part was a dial completely covered with luminous coating. The high radiance—or radiation—of the dial and the hands was due to a special mixture that included zinc sulfate and radium bromide.

The latter also helped give the watch its name, Radiomir, and subjected its wearer to a dose of radioactivity. As if these sailors were not in enough danger already!

Ebel

Sportwave Diver, steel, Ebel caliber 120 (base ETA 2892-A2), water-resistant to 657 feet (200 m), unidirectional rotating diver's bezel, from 2006

Ebel

Discovery, steel, automatic, Ebel caliber 080 (based on Lémania 8815), water-resistant to 657 feet (200 m), unidirectional rotating diver's bezel, from 1999

Doxa

Sub 750 T Professional, steel, automatic, ETA caliber 28245-2, water-resistant to 2460 feet (750 m), unidirectional rotating diver's bezel with decompression table, from 2006

Doxa

Sub 600 T-Graph, steel, automatic, ETA caliber 2894-2, chronograph, water-resistant to 1970 feet (600 m), unidirectional rotating diver's bezel with decompression table, from 2006

These servicemen were part of a kind of swimmers' combat unit within the Italian navy. Two frogmen rode a steerable torpedo, a kind of underwater motorbike, in order to creep into allied harbors and destroy enemy shipping with explosives. These special watch-equipped divers had their most spectacular mission in 1941, when they sank three important British navy ships in the harbor of Alexandria. In 1943, the Florentine watchmakers designed a chronograph intended for navy officers. This watch was known as Mare Nostrum, the ancient Romans' name for the Mediterranean. However, because of the Second World War, this project never got past the prototype stage.

In the early 1950s, Panerai delivered the Luminor model to the army, the later replacement for the Radiomir. The shape of the case and the design of the dial remained the same. The gamma ray-emitting radium, however, was replaced by the less dangerous

Eterna
Porsche Design titanium diver's watch, titanium, automatic, EternaMatic caliber 633 (base ETA 2824-2), water-resistant to 985 feet (300 m), unidirectional rotating diver's bezel, from 1999

Enicar
Super Dive Sherpa, steel, automatic, caliber AR 1145, unidirectional rotating inner diver's bezel, water-resistant to 328 feet (100 m), from 1970

Eterna
KonTiki Diver, steel, automatic, ETA caliber 2892-A2, water-resistant to 328 feet (100 m), unidirectional rotating inner diver's bezel, from 2006

Jacques Etoile
Atlantis, steel, automatic, ETA caliber 2824-2, water-resistant to 1640 feet (500 m), movement magnetic field protected, unidirectional rotating diver's bezel, from 2006

Fortis
Official Cosmonaut's Sports Diver,
steel, automatic, ETA caliber 2836-2,
water-resistant to 657 feet (200 m),
unidirectional rotating diver's bezel,
from 1999

tritium. The water resistance was also considerably improved, which was due not least to the very specialized crown seal, typical to this day of a Panerai Luminor. This was a crescent-shaped protective cover over the crown, with a little built-in lever. In order to set or wind the watch, the lever had to be released. When closed, it compressed the crown seal so much that no water could force its way in and the crown became immovable.

Military requirements continued to characterize the development of the diver's watch. In the 1950s, Captain Robert Maloubier was commissioned by the French Ministry of Defense to set up a new diving combat unit, the *Nageurs du Combat*. For this purpose, he had to find not only the right people, but also the right equipment. An extremely sturdy diver's watch, for example, reliable and precise at depths of almost 3330 feet (100 meters). Interestingly, his diver's watch project ended

Hublot
Professional, steel/yellow gold, automatic, ETA caliber
2892-2, water-resistant to 985 feet (300 m), from 1999

Fortis
B-42 Diver Day Date, steel,
automatic, ETA caliber 2836-2,
water-resistant to 657 feet (200 m),
unidirectional rotating diver's bezel,
from 2006

Glashütte Original
Sport Evolution, steel, automatic,
Glashütte Original caliber 10-30,
water-resistant to 657 feet (200 m),
from 1999

Girard-Perregaux
Sea Hawk II Pro, titanium,
automatic, GFP caliber 033RO
(based on GP 3300), movement
magnetic field protection, water-
resistant to 9850 feet (3000 m),
power reserve indicator, case with
two helium valves, from 2006

Glycine

Lagunare LCC 1000, steel, automatic, ETA caliber 2824-2, water-resistant to 985 feet (300 m), C.O.S.C. certified chronometer, unidirectional rotating diver's bezel, from 2006

IWC

ATM Aquatimer, steel, automatic, IWC caliber 8541B, water-resistant to 985 feet (300 m), unidirectional rotating inner diver's bezel, from 2006

IWC

Aquatimer Automatic 2000, titanium, automatic, IWC caliber 30110 (base ETA 2892-A2), water-resistant to 6560 feet (2000 m), unidirectional rotating diver's bezel, from 2006

IWC

GST Aquatimer, titanium, automatic, IWC caliber C37524 (base ETA 2892-A2), water-resistant to 6560 feet (2000 m), unidirectional rotating diver's bezel, from 2006

IWC

Aquatimer Split Minute Chronograph, titanium, automatic, IWC caliber 79740 (base ETA 7750), water-resistant to 394 feet (120 m), chronograph with split minute hand, unidirectional rotating inner diver's bezel, from 2006

IWC

Aquatimer Automatic, steel, automatic, IWC caliber 30110 (base ETA 2892-A2), water-resistant to 3280 feet (1000 m), unidirectional rotating inner diver's bezel, from 2006

177

up in the Swiss Jura, with the clockmakers Blancpain, who developed a timepiece known as "Fifty Fathoms," after the depth required.

A fathom, the traditional depth measurement of Western navigation, is equivalent to 6.01 feet (1.829 meters). Maloubier therefore demanded guaranteed water resistance to a diving depth of 300 feet (91.45 meters), plus extremely good readability and a diving time bezel that could be used to determine diving and decompression times more exactly to within five minutes: That is to say, an instrument important for the diver's safety, that could be used to apportion the limited supplies of breathable air in diver's tanks. For this reason, too, Maloubier demanded that the bezel could only be moved counterclockwise. Therefore, if

Krieger
Hammerhead Pro Diver's Chronometer, steel, automatic, C.O.S.C. certified chronometer, water-resistant to 985 feet (300 m), from 1999

Jaeger-LeCoultre
Memovox Polaris, steel, automatic, caliber 425, unidirectional rotating inner diver's bezel, alarm function, water-resistant to 985 feet (300 m), from 1966

Limes
Endurance 1000, steel, automatic, ETA caliber 2824, water-resistant to 3280 feet (1000 m), unidirectional rotating diver's bezel, from 2006

Longines
Automatic Diver's Watch, steel, automatic, caliber 431, unidirectional rotating inner diver's bezel, from 1965

Longines
Automatic Diver's Watch, steel, automatic, caliber 290, unidirectional rotating inner diver's bezel, from 1965

he bezel were accidentally moved, this would then lead to apparent increase in the time spent on the dive and to an earlier ascent than scheduled.

Maloubier's specifications also demanded good legibility, and Blancpain put this into practice with large numbers and hands coated with tritium. The watch passed its test on November 20, 1953 with flying colors. The French captain certified the excellence of the Swiss clockmakers' work with a plain, "*Bon*". The reliability, workmanship, precision, and ease of use of the "Fifty Fathoms" became widely known, so that both the elite US Navy Seals unit and the newly formed German military frogmen's unit decided in favor of Blancpain.

This watch was in official use by the German *Bundeswehr* until 1994. Then it was superseded by the Ocean, commissioned by the German military from IWC. The watchmakers from Schaffhausen in Germany won an official tender, and in the spring of 1980 they received

a 30-page set of specifications which set out requirements such as precision, shock-proof qualities, temperature characteristics, thickness, and amagnetic properties. The last turned out to be a true challenge, as Jürgen King, then technical director of IWC, recalls: "We had some experience with military watches, but neither we nor any other company had ever made amagnetic watches." The background to this demand was that the detonators of certain mines react not only to pressure or sound, but also to the weakest of magnetic fields, such as may be caused by the movements of quartz watches. This meant that this new development must neither create nor change magnetic fields. Even the experienced Schaffhausen watchmakers had to do some basic research here, and work in unconventional ways. Because buildings are, for the most part, not free of disruptive magnetic fields, King took the test candidates and their equipment into his own garden and carried out measurements there. IWC was supported in its development and materials research by scientists at the

Marcello C.
Tridente Chronograph, steel, automatic, ETA caliber 7750, water-resistant to 985 feet (300 m), unidirectional rotating diver's bezel, from 2006

Marcello C.
Nettuno 3, steel, automatic, ETA caliber 2824-2, water-resistant to 985 feet (300 m), unidirectional rotating diver's bezel, from 2006

Marcello C.
Nettuno, steel, automatic, ETA caliber 2824-2, water-resistant to 657 feet (200 m), unidirectional rotating diver's bezel, from 1999

Marcello C.
Nettuno Chronograph steel, automatic, ETA caliber 7750, water-resistant to 985 feet (300 m), unidirectional rotating diver's bezel, from 2006

179

Mido
Ocean Star Sport Diver, steel,
automatic, ETA caliber 2836-2,
water-resistant to 657 feet (200 m),
unidirectional rotating diver's bezel,
from 2006

Nivada
Depthomatic, steel, automatic, ETA caliber 2472,
water-resistant to 657 feet (200 m), integrated mechanical
depth gauge, unidirectional rotating diver's bezel, from 2006

Mühle Glashütte
Nautic-Timer, steel, automatic, ETA caliber 2824-2,
water-resistant to 6562 feet (2000 m), unidirectional
rotating divers' bezel, from 2006

Mido
All Dial Diver, steel, automatic,
ETA caliber 2836-2, water-resistant
to 657 feet (200 m), unidirectional
rotating inner diver's bezel,
from 2006

University of Lausanne. The automatic works were to function like any other automatic works, only with tried and tested parts being replaced by amagnetic ones. These included the balance spring, made from a special alloy (niobium-zirconium). There is no further information officially available, because the amagnetic mine diver's watch is, just like the ordinary diver's automatic watch and the frogman's watch with quartz movement, part of the navy's current equipment, and as such is issued a NATO supply number and falls under secrecy regulations.

King is, however, able to say this much: "We were required to make a very hard-wearing watch. But until we got there, there was a lot of waste metal." The requirement for a robust case and glass led to a seal tighter than any that had been attained up to that point. The Ocean could withstand up to 200 bar (units of atmosphere pressure), corresponding to a depth of 6560 feet (2000 meters). The civilian version of the Ocean, designed, as the military watches were, by Ferdinand Alexander Porsche, was also given 2000 as an addition to its name for the same reason.

When the Blancpain was becoming a little elderly, but the IWC was not yet finished, many navy frogmen decided on the first watch actually designed for sporting divers: the Doxa Sub 300. The unmistakable feature of a Doxa diver's watch was and still is the orange dial. The spiritual father of this dial is considered to be Urs Eschle, Doxa's chief research and development man at the time. He dived in Lake Neufchatel with four plaques in different colors (turquoise, yellow, red, orange) and, based on the best legibility at

Omega

Seamaster Automatic 600 m Ploprof, steel monocoque, automatic, Omega caliber, water-resistant to 1970 feet (600 m), unidirectional rotating diver's bezel, made for professional divers (hence the name *Plongeurs Professionels*—Ploprof), from 1972

Omega

Seamaster 300, steel, automatic, Omega caliber 565, water-resistant to 985 feet (300 m), unidirectional rotating diver's bezel, from 1969

Omega

Seamaster Planet Ocean Co-Axial, steel, automatic, Omega caliber 2500C (based on Omega 1120), water-resistant to 1970 feet (600 m), unidirectional rotating diver's bezel, case with helium valve, from 2006

Omega

Seamaster Chrono Diver 300 m, steel, automatic, Omega caliber 3301, chronograph, C.O.S.C. certified chronometer, water-resistant to 985 feet (300 m), unidirectional rotating diver's bezel, case with helium valve, from 2006

Omega

Seamaster Professional Diver, steel, automatic, Omega caliber 1120, C.O.S.C. certified chronometer, water-resistant to 985 feet (300 m), unidirectional rotating diver's bezel, from 1999

181

great depth, decided on orange, the color of the 1970s. As a special feature, the designers equipped the bezel not just with a minutes ring, but also with a decompression table.

Alongside the total dive time, decompression is the most important time information for a diver. The extreme diver and scientist, Hannes Keller, was keenly aware of this and, together with the researchers of the clockmakers Vulcain, he designed a new diver's watch. The Cricket Nautical was the first diver's alarm with an integral decompression calculator, which had an acoustic alarm that would function even underwater. This alarm was to signal the preset time for surfacing.

Keller had big plans, as he wrote in a letter dated July 3, 1961 to the Vulcain management: "I am happy to be able to report that I have succeeded in setting a new world record in diving in Brissago on the afternoon of June 28, 1961." With his diving partner Kenneth McLeish, science editor for the American magazine, *Life*, Keller dove 728 feet (222 meters) down into Lago Maggiore; both men were wearing Cricket Nauticals on their wrists. In a letter, Keller is full of praise for the timepieces, which were subjected to "extraordinary stresses" such as high temperatures and differences in pressure. "Both watches performed excellently in the trials. I also tested the alarm mechanism of one of the two watches. The sound could be clearly heard, even

Oris

TT1 Master Diver, titanium, automatic, Oris caliber 649 (base ETA 2836-2), regulator display, water-resistant to 3280 feet (1000 m), unidirectional rotating diver's bezel, case with helium valve, from 2006

Oris

TT1 Divers Titanium Chronograph, titanium, automatic, Oris caliber 674 (base ETA 7750), water-resistant to 985 feet (300 m), unidirectional rotating diver's bezel, case with helium valve, from 2006

Oris

TT1 Divers Titanium, titanium, automatic, Oris caliber 633 (base ETA 2824-2), water-resistant to 3280 feet (1000 m), unidirectional rotating diver's bezel, case with helium valve, from 2006

Oris

TT1 Divers Titanium Date, titanium, Oris caliber 633 (base ETA 2824-2), dial completely covered with luminous coating, water-resistant to 985 feet (300 m), unidirectional rotating diver's bezel, case with helium valve, from 2006

Panerai

Luminor Egittica, steel, hand winding, Angelus eight-day movement, frogman's watch for the Egyptian navy. Some 50 of these were made, from approx. 1956

Panerai

Luminor Submersible 2500, titanium, automatic, Panerai caliber OP III, C.O.S.C. certified chronometer, water-resistant to 3280 feet (1000 m), unidirectional rotating diver's bezel, from 2006

Panerai

Radiomir Brevattato, steel, hand winding, frogman's watch from the Italian navy, from 1938

Three chunky models from the early days of divers' watches

Paul Picot
Le Plongeur C-Type Date, steel,
automatic, ETA caliber 2824-2,
C.O.S.C. certified chronometer,
water-resistant to 985 feet (300 m),
unidirectional rotating diver's bezel,
from 2006

Paul Picot
Le Plongeur C-Type Chronograph,
steel, automatic, ETA caliber 7752,
C.O.S.C. certified chronometer,
water-resistant to 985 feet (300 m),
unidirectional rotating diver's bezel,
from 2006

Poljot
Red October, steel, automatic,
Vostok caliber 2416.B, water-resistant
to 985 feet (300 m), unidirectional
rotating diver's bezel, from 2006

though my diving suit was fully closed..." The legibility of the dial and the decompression table also met with Keller's full satisfaction, leading him to the following conclusion: "With regard to this extraordinary performance, I have no doubt that the Vulcain Cricket Nautical Diver's Watch will be a great success on the market and that the watch will provide many divers with the same inestimable service that it has given us during these difficult tests."

It was not to be the last time that an extreme diver cooperated in the development of a

diver's watch. On July 6, 1999, Mario Weidner set a record in the Arctic Sea. Weidner, who comes from Frankfurt am Main in Germany, achieved a dive to a depth of 212 feet (64.5 meters) in the ice-cold waters of the 81st parallel. Over his thick suit, he wore a watch that also came from Frankfurt, the Sinn Chronograph 203. The professional diver later commented for the record: "The good legibility of the blue dial in combination with the slightly domed sapphire crystal, especially under water, was a particularly positive feature." Sinn technicians who had accompanied the diver on his journey also noted that for the first time in practical application, a special oil performed exactly as promised. Despite the great cold, the running of the automatic movement never diverged from its target values. And the case did not allow a single drop of Arctic water to penetrate. This meant that the Model 203 deserved the official addition of "Arktis" to its name.

An unofficial nickname, though one well-known even among non-divers, was given to a very popular diver's watch. The Omega Seamaster Professional is known in many quarters simply as the Bond watch, because it had to survive many difficult challenges on the

wrist of Agent 007. The Seamaster made its first appearance in a James Bond film in *Goldeneye* in 1995, where it had two neat details built into its case: a laser that shot out of the helium escape valve and a remote detonator for bombs which, after activating, set off a blinking light at 12 o'clock on the dial. Bond used the laser to cut open the floor in the armored express in order to free himself from the clutches of Alec Trevelyan (the renegade agent 006, who in the film wore a Seamaster himself—though an older model). The detonator came into its own somewhat later, when it was time to set off the bomb with which the Cuban command center for the secret satellites activated by Goldeneye was to be destroyed.

Rado
Original diver, steel, automatic, ETA caliber 2824-2, water-resistant to 985 feet (300 m), unidirectional rotating inner diver's bezel, from 2006

Rolex
Oyster Perpetual Submariner, steel, automatic, Rolex caliber 1520, water-resistant to 657 feet (200 m), unidirectional rotating diver's bezel, service watch for Royal Marines frogmen, from 1969

Rolex
Oyster Perpetual Submariner, steel, automatic, Rolex caliber 1030, water-resistant to 657 feet (200 m), unidirectional rotating diver's bezel, from 1959

Rolex
Oyster Perpetual Submariner, steel, automatic, water-resistant to 657 feet (200 m), unidirectional rotating diver's bezel, from 1964

In the 1997 Bond film, *Tomorrow Never Dies*, the Seamaster acted as a detonator once again, setting off a grenade on the stealth boat belonging to media mogul Elliot Carver, the villain of the film, making it visible on radar. In *The World is Not Enough*, the watch twice plays a decisive part. The first time, a strong light source, radiating from the dial of the watch is used by Bond to gain a view of the situation inside his "inflatable" jacket airbag, in which he finds protection from the avalanche thundering over him. The second lifesaver was a grappling hook concealed in the case, allowing Bond to free himself and Dr. Christmas Jones from a bunker. The miniature grappling hook shoots out from the crown and causes the rotating

Seamaster bezel to race around furiously; as soon as the hook has caught firmly, the bezel turns slowly in the opposite direction, once more rolling up the wire within the watch case and drawing Bond and his companion upwards to safety.

Important Dates in the History of Divers' Watches

1927: Rolex, with the Oyster, presents the first water-resistant watch case. As public proof of and advertising for this novelty, Rolex equips the swimmer Mercedes Gleitze with an Oyster, and she swims the English Channel with the watch on her wrist.

Left: Recognizable at first glance:
three of Rolex's divers' chronometers

Scalfaro
North Shore Chronograph TriCompax, steel, automatic, ADK caliber 150 (base ETA 7750), water-resistant to 328 feet (100 m), unidirectional rotating diver's bezel, from 2006

Rolex
Submariner Date, steel, automatic, Rolex caliber 3135, C.O.S.C. certified chronometer, water-resistant to 4002 feet (1220 m), unidirectional rotating diver's bezel, from 1999

Scalfaro
North Shore Second Time Zone, steel, automatic, ADK caliber 148 (base ETA 2892-2), 24-hour indicator (second zone time), water-resistant to 985 feet (300 m), unidirectional rotating diver's bezel, from 2006

Rolex
Oyster Perpetual Sea-Dweller 4000, steel, automatic, Rolex caliber 3135, C.O.S.C. certified chronometer, water-resistant to 4002 feet (1220 m), unidirectional rotating diver's bezel, helium valve in case, from 2006

187

Sinn

Diver's Chronograph, steel, automatic, ETA caliber 7750, water-resistant to 985 feet (300 m), case completely filled with argon gas, unidirectional rotating diver's bezel, screw-down push buttons, from 1999

Sinn

Einsatzzeitmesser (EZM 1), titanium, automatic, Lémania caliber 5100, water-resistant to 985 feet (300 m), chronograph, unidirectional rotating diver's bezel, from 1999

1932: Omega constructs its first water-resistant diver's watch, the "Marine."

1936: Officine constructs the first prototype of a diver's watch, building a Rolex movement into the case of a Panerai depth meter.

1953: Blancpain launches the "Fifty Fathoms," water-resistant to almost 328 feet (100 meters) (50 fathoms = 300 feet/91.45 meters). It was first made for the French navy. In 1959, frogmen of the German *Bundeswehr* were equipped with this watch. In the same year, the Zodiac Sea Wolf came out, exclusively issued for combat divers (US Seals). 1953 is also the birthday of what is probably the best-known diver's watch in the world: the Rolex Submariner.

1954: The Rolex Submariner is certified to 657 feet (200 meters) diving depth.

1956: The Blancpain Fifty Fathoms, thanks to its appearance in the Jacques Cousteau film, *The Silent World*, becomes known among sports divers. The Tudor Sub, with Rolex movement, appears in two versions, for 328 and 657 feet (100 and 200 meters) depth.

1957: The Omega Seamaster is launched (water-resistant to 657 feet/200 meters).

1958: The Breitling Superocean, also water-resistant to 657 feet (200 meters), appears on the market.

1960: As proof of its competence, Rolex manufactures a one-off timepiece with particularly thick glass, which, fastened to the outer shell of Jacques Piccard's bathyscaphe *Trieste*, survived a 35,815 feet (10,916 meter) dive unharmed.

1961: The Swiss diving expert, Hannes Keller, achieves a record diving depth of 722 feet (220 meters) with the diver's alarm Vulcain Cricket Nautical.

Sinn

Arktis diver's chronograph, steel, automatic, ETA caliber 7750, water-resistant to 985 feet (300 m), case completely filled with argon gas, lubrication with special oil for temperatures between –113 degrees Fahrenheit to 176 degrees Fahrenheit (–45 to 80 degrees C), unidirectional rotating diver's bezel, from 2006

Stowa

Seatime, steel, automatic, ETA caliber 2824, water-resistant to 985 feet (300 m), unidirectional rotating diver's bezel, from 2006

TAG Heuer

Aquaracer Automatic Chronograph, steel, automatic, TAG Heuer caliber 16 (base ETA 7750), water-resistant to 985 feet (300 m), unidirectional rotating diver's bezel, from 2006

Sinn

Einsatzzeitmesser (EZM 2), steel, quartz, ETA caliber 955.612, water-resistant to all reachable diving depths, case completely filled with oil, unidirectional rotating diver's bezel, from 2006

Sinn

U1 diver's watch, submarine steel, automatic, ETA caliber 2824-2, water-resistant to 3280 feet (1000 m), unidirectional rotating diver's bezel, from 2006

Sinn

U2/EZM5 diver's watch, submarine steel, automatic, ETA caliber 2893-2, 24-hour indicator (second zone time), water-resistant to 6560 feet (2000 m), unidirectional rotating diver's bezel, from 2006

TAG Heuer

Aquagraph Automatic Chronograph, steel, automatic, TAG Heuer caliber 60 (based on Dubois-Dépraz 2073), water-resistant to 1640 feet (500 m), push buttons functional to 1640 feet (500 m) depth, stop-second and stop-minute from the center, unidirectional rotating diver's bezel, from 2006

Tissot
Visodate Seamaster T12, steel, automatic, caliber 784-2, unidirectional rotating inner diver's bezel, from 1975

1963: The Aquastar Benthos 500 is launched and accompanies the divers of the Précontinente-Experimente from Jacques-Yves Cousteau's team.

1964: The first two divers' watches that can reach a depth of 3280 feet (1000 meters) are introduced. One is the reworked Aquastar/Lemania Benthos and the other the Caribbean 1000.

1965: The Doxa brand is the first to target sports divers directly and introduces the Doxa Sub 300 at the Basle Clock and Watch Fair—the first diver's watch to have a clearly legible orange-colored dial. Jaeger-LeCoultre presents the diver's alarm Polaris with an inner diver's bezel. Seiko introduces the first Japanese diver's watch (water-resistant to 492 feet/150 meters).

1966: With the Favre-Leuba Bathy 50, Henry Favre brings the first diver's watch with a Boyle-Marriot depth meter on to the market. In the USA, the watch is known as the Bathy 160 (because of its 160 feet diving depth).

1967: The bezel on the Doxa Sub 300, developed in cooperation with US divers, is patented. It gives information on decompression times. In the USA, the Doxa is now used by the military. Rolex makes a Submariner with helium valve for professional use (Comex). Seiko improves the water resistance of its diver's watch and now calls it the Professional 300. IWC launches its first diver's watch, the Aquatimer.

1969: Doxa's 200 T-Graph is the first diver's chronograph with a stopwatch mechanism which can be used underwater.

1970: For eight days, the new Omega Seamaster 600 accompanies three Comex divers in saturation diving in 820 feet (250 meters) of water off Corsica. Diving pioneer Claude Wesley, in a dive in the Red Sea, tests prototypes by Doxa and Rolex with helium valves. In the same year, Doxa brings the production-ready Sub 600 Conquistador (with helium valve) on to the market.

Tissot
Seastar 1000 Automatic, steel, automatic, ETA caliber 2824-2, water-resistant to 985 feet (300 m), unidirectional rotating diver's bezel, from 2006

Right: A striking appearance: Diver's watch by Harry Winston. This jeweler and producer of decorative watches also understands decidedly masculine design

TAG Heuer
Kirium Chronometer, steel, automatic, ETA caliber 2892-A2, C.O.S.C. certified chronometer, water-resistant to 657 feet (200 m), unidirectional rotating diver's bezel, from 1999

Tissot
PR 100 Divermatic, steel, automatic, ETA caliber 2836-2, water-resistant to 492 feet (150 m), unidirectional rotating diver's bezel, from 1999

Tudor

Oyster Prince Submariner, steel, automatic, water-resistant to 657 feet (200 m), unidirectional rotating diver's bezel, from 1965

Left: To make a high-quality watch suitable for serious diving use, a great deal of time and money must be invested in the technology

Tudor

Prince Date Hydronaut, steel, automatic, ETA caliber 2824-2, water-resistant to 657 feet (200 m), unidirectional rotating diver's bezel, from 2006

1971: Omega makes the Seamaster 1000. The Rolex Seadweller with helium valve (water-resistant to 2001 feet/610 meters) makes its appearance.

1972: Omega brings out its first chronograph that can also be used underwater (water-resistant to 394 feet/120 meters).

1973: The Doxa Sub 250 makes its appearance, the first watch with the crown at the four o'clock position.

1975: Seiko doubles the diving depth of its diver's watch to 1970 feet (600 meters) and is the first to use titanium in the construction of the case. The rubber strap, with its three expansion folds, is another innovation.

1980: IWC is commissioned by the German *Bundeswehr* to develop and make a diver's watch. The Nautilus brand introduces functional divers' watches at favorable prices: The Professional, with a diving depth of 1640 feet (500 meters) for around 500 German marks and the Superpro, with a diving depth of 3280 feet (1000 meters) for around 1000 marks.

1983: Sinn launches its first diver's watch, water-resistant to 3280 feet (1000 meters).

1984: The German *Bundeswehr's* research and development contract leads to the creation of the IWC Ocean 2000, the first diver's watch in the world that is water-resistant to 6560 feet (2000 meters). It is made in a military version (for the German navy) and a civilian version. A parallel amagnetic version is developed for mine divers, water resistant to 985 feet (300 meters).

1985: The Citizen Aquaband is the first analog diver's watch with a digital electronic depth meter. Seiko also brings out a diver's watch with electronic depth meter, which is, however, considerably larger than the Citizen.

1986: TAG Heuer launches the Super Professional model for dive depths of 3280 feet (1000 meters).

Tutima

DI 300, titanium, automatic, ETA caliber 2836-2, water-resistant to 985 feet (300 m), unidirectional rotating diver's bezel, from 2006

Ulysse Nardin

Maxi Marine Diver Chronometer, steel, automatic, Ulysse Nardin caliber UN26 (base ETA 2892), C.O.S.C. certified chronometer, water-resistant to 985 feet (300 m), from 2006

193

Universal Genève
Golden Tech Diver, steel/gold, automatic, Universal Genève caliber 71, unidirectional rotating diver's bezel, water-resistant to 328 feet (100 m), from 1999

Louis Vuitton
Tambour Diving Automatique XL, rose gold, automatic, ETA caliber 2895-2, water-resistant to 985 feet (300 m), unidirectional rotating diver's bezel, from 2006

1987: Casio also introduces a watch with an electronic depth meter, but with fully digital display only, in contrast to Citizen.

1988: The Citizen Aqualand continues to be improved and now has a second display and a more compact sensor.

1989: The Rolex Submariner now has a diver's bezel that rotates counterclockwise only. The Citizen Aqualand is now also available with analog depth meter display. This promotes it to become the favorite watch among sports divers.

1993: Omega designs a dive chronometer for depths of up to 9850 feet (300 meters). The free-diver Roland Specker, wearing this watch, achieves a world record depth of 262 feet (80 meters) in Lake Neufchatel. In the same year, Omega launches the Seamaster Professional, a watch still up-to-date today, with its helium valve. An appearance in a James Bond film causes the Seamaster to become known as the Bond watch.

1995: Breitling makes the Colt Superocean for a dive depth of up to 4920 feet (1500 meters).

1996: Kienzle breaks the Rolex world depth record with The Deepest. This record-breaker is a simple plastic timepiece filled with oil to stabilize it. Its depth capacity is certified to 39,370 feet (12,000 meters). Sector introduces the Diving Team 1000 for depths of up to 3280 feet (1000 meters).

1997: The Finnish manufacturer Suunto presents the Spyder, the first diving computer in watch format, which becomes very popular among divers.

1998: IWC introduces the GST Aquatimer for depths of up to 6560 feet (2000 meters).

1999: IWC launches the Deep One, the first divers' watch with a mechanical depth gauge and a split-second hand. It indicates depths of up to 148 feet (45 meters) and is water-resistant to 492 feet (150 meters).

Vulcain
Cricket Nautical, steel, hand winding, caliber MSR S 2, water-resistant to 985 feet (300 m), dial center with bidirectional rotation for dive decompression times, alarm, from 1969

2000: Ulysse Nardin presents the first mechanical diver's watch with a perpetual calendar.

2002: Breitling launches the Avenger Seawolf for depths of up to 9850 feet (3000 meters) and holds the current world record for mechanical watches.

2003: TAG Heuer launches the 2000 Aquagraph model, the first diver's chronograph that remains functional at depths of up to 1640 feet (500 meters). Baume & Mercier (CapeLand S XXl 1000) and Oris (TT1 Master Diver) bring out watches for depths of up to 3280 feet (1000 meters); the new Bulgari models (Diagono Professional Scuba Diving 2000) and Mühle (SAR Rescue Timer) are tested to 657 feet (200 meters). Doxa begins production of the Sub 600 again, after the limited edition of the Sub 300 sold out in a very short time.

2004: IWC introduces the Aquatimer Split Minute Chronograph, the first watch with a split-second hand that can be used underwater.

2006: Eterna launches the KonTiki Diver, a diver's watch with a unique case structure. The watch can only be adjusted with the case open.

Harry Winston
Ocean, platinum, automatic,
GP caliber 3106, diver's bezel
(undirectional rotation),
water-resistant to 328 feet
(100 m), from 1999

Vulcain
Nautical, steel, hand winding, Vulcain
caliber V-10, water-resistant to 985 feet
(300 m), dial center with bidirectional
rotation for dive decompression times,
alarm, from 2006

Zenith
Rainbow Elite diver's watch, steel,
automatic, Zenith caliber Elite,
unidirectional rotating diver's bezel,
water-resistant to 657 feet (200 m),
from 1999

195

5. GMT AND WORLD TIME WATCHES

In other countries, they often do things differently. Time, for instance. If you are in business, a jetsetter, or globetrotter, it's a good idea to wear a watch that tells you what the time is when you are away, but won't let you forget the time at home.

Alpina
Avalanche GMT, steel, quartz,
24-hour indicator (second zone time),
from 2006

Baume and Mercier
Classima Executives GMT XL, steel,
automatic, BM caliber 11893-2
(base ETA 2893-2) 24-hour indicator
(second zone time), from 2006

The world is a sphere, more or less. Because this sphere turns around the sun, only half of it is ever lit at any one time. Today this seems obvious, but until the mid-nineteenth century little attention was paid to this fact, according to which time would have to be different in different places across the world.

In Germany alone, each of the many principalities and duchies had its own time. This could perhaps be tolerated in the age of stagecoaches, but after the introduction of the transregional—and above all, much faster—railways, led to utter chaos. Just imagine a rail timetable that had to take account of more than 30 different local times!

In a country such as Germany this caused difficulties enough, but in countries that extended farther to the east and west, such as Russia, for example, or the USA, it led to even greater problems. After lengthy international negotiations, there was agreement in 1884 on

Audemars Piguet
Millenary Dual Time, yellow gold, automatic, AP caliber 2129, additional 12-hour indicator (second zone time), power reserve indicator, from 1999

Blancpain
GMT, steel, automatic, Blancpain caliber 5A50, 24-hour indicator (second zone time), rotating bezel with 24-hour time division (third zone time), from 1999

the division of the earth into 24 time zones. This regulation, however, was not accepted until the beginning of the last century. Established in the UK to standardize national railway timetables, and later adopted internationally, this regulation was known as GMT (Greenwich Mean Time) since the Greenwich Meridian (0° longitude) is the starting point for the time zones. It is now known as UTC, Coordinated Universal Time, the main feature of which is the use of the 24-hour clock as applied to the time zones.

GMT and UTC are in general use today in the clockmaking industry as terms for timepieces covering two or more time zones. The Rolex GMT Master II, for example, has a 24-hour hand constantly set to home time, but also, if selected, GMT. Local time is shown by the hour hand, which can be set without moving the minute hand. The second hand also continues to run, thus not losing a single second for the watch-lover. The IWC Spitfire UTC functions in a similar manner, the only difference being that here the 24-hour display is shown in a semicircular cut-out of the dial.

One small snag with GMT watches is that the owner needs to know the time difference

Blancpain
Léman Réveil GMT, red gold, automatic, Blancpain caliber 1241, 24-hour indicator (second zone time), alarm function, from 2006

Blancpain
Le Brassus GMT Moon Phase, red gold, automatic, Blancpain caliber 67A6, 24-hour indicator (second zone time), from 2006

Rainer Brand
Panama Dual Time, steel, automatic, ETA caliber 2892-2, additional 12-hour indicator (second zone time), from 1999

Rainer Brand
Panama Dual Time, steel, automatic, ETA caliber 2892-2, additional 12-hour indicator (second zone time), from 2006

Breguet
Marine GMT, yellow gold, automatic, Breguet caliber 563, world time indicator, from 1999

199

Carl F. Bucherer
Patravi Travel Tec GMT, steel, automatic, CFB caliber 1901, 24-hour indicator and rotating bezel under glass with 24-hour divisions (second and third zone times), chronograph, from 2006

Carl F. Bucherer
Patravi Chronograph GMT, steel, automatic, CFB caliber 1901, 24-hour indicator and rotating bezel with 24-hour divisions (second and third zone times), chronograph, from 2006

Breitling
B-1, steel, quartz, Breitling caliber 78, 24-hour Indicator (second zone time), chronograph, alarm function, C.O.S.C. certified chronometer, from 2006

Breitling
Colt GMT, steel, automatic, Breitling caliber 32 (base ETA 2893-2), 24-hour indicator (second zone time), C.O.S.C. certified chronometer, from 2006

between home and local time. Going right around the whole world (in timekeeping terms) requires a world time watch. Its decisive external feature is an adjustable ring with the name of one place within each of the 24 time zones of our world, and in most cases also a 24-hour indicator. It sounds simple, but technically it is not without snags, which arise as soon as we come to the setting of date and time. When crossing the date line in the Pacific, for example, the date display also needs to be put back, along with the city and 24-hour bezel.

Bulgari

Diagono Professional GMT Flyback, steel, automatic, Dubois-Dépraz caliber 21340, 24-hour indicator (second zone time), chronograph with Flyback function, C.O.S.C. certified chronometer, from 2006

Bulova

Edition, steel, automatic, ETA caliber 2892, 24-hour indicator (second zone time), power reserve indicator, from 1999

Bulgari

Bulgari GMT, steel, automatic, caliber MVA 060, 24-hour indicator (second zone time), from 1999

Chopard

L.U.C. GMT, white gold, automatic, L.U.C. caliber 4/96/1-H1, 24-hour indicator (second zone time), C.O.S.C. certified chronometer, from 2006

Corum

Classical GMT, steel, automatic, Corum caliber CO 983983, (base ETA 2892-A2 with module), 24-hour indicator (second zone time), rotating bezel with names of reference cities for time zones, C.O.S.C. certified chronometer, from 2006

Chronoswiss

Tora, yellow gold, automatic, Chronoswiss caliber C.123, 24-hour indicator (second zone time), from 1999

Cuervo y Sobrinos

Prominente D.T., steel, automatic, ETA caliber 2671, additional 12-hour indicator (second zone time), from 2006

Clever engineers and watch designers have come up with all kinds of mechanisms and levers to solve this problem. These are used by means of push buttons on the case, a second crown or a rotating bezel.

Individual world time

In 2004, Vogard brought a watch on to the market that has (so far) exclusively devoted itself to the topic of "world time." The mechanism, devised by Vogard and now patented, allows the simple operation of a bezel, well-known from divers' watches and chronographs, to set the desired time zone. The design is based on seeing the case, movement and bezel as a single functioning unit.

A noticeable exterior feature of the design by Thomas Prescher, and at the same time a decisive functioning part, is the crescent-shaped lever which moves on a screwed-in hinge by the lower right strap holder. In the rest position, the lever lies in an enclosure within the case.

Davosa
Vireo Dual Time, steel, automatic, ETA caliber 2893, 24-hour indicator (second zone time), from 2006

De Grisogono
Instrumento Doppio Tre, steel, automatic, ETA caliber 2892-A2 with module and hand movement at rear, additional 12-hour indicator on back of case, from 2006

De Witt
Académia Double Fuseau, red gold, automatic, De Witt caliber DW 2001 (base ETA 2892-A2), 24-hour indicator (second zone time), from 2006

Jaquet Droz
Les Deux Fuseaux, white gold, automatic, Jaquet Droz caliber 5L60, 24-hour indicator (second zone time), from 2006

Dubey & Schaldenbrand
Diplomatic Classic, steel, automatic,
ETA caliber 2892-A2, 24-hour
indicator (second zone time),
from 1999

If the lever is moved out from the case, a button pops out, activated by a powerful spring, to protrude by about 0.1 inches (1.8 mm) from the case. This then releases the bezel, previously held by a projection on the flank of the button.

The bezel (city ring) is available from Vogard marked with various destinations, such as major cities, airports, or even golf courses. You can even have one-off versions with a customized selection of places. You can have a bezel made with the names of places you have visited, of cities in which your friends live, or just have Berlin replace Paris for "Central European Time."

Dubey & Schaldenbrand
Aerodyn Duo, steel, automatic, ETA caliber 2893, 24-hour
indicator (second zone time), from 2006

Roger Dubuis
Golden Square Dual Time, rose gold,
automatic, RD caliber 5747, additional
12-hour indicator (second zone time),
from 2006

Dubey & Schaldenbrand
Diplomatic GMT, steel, automatic,
ETA caliber 2892-A2, 24-hour
indicator (second zone time),
from 1999

Enicar
Sherpa Jet Automatic, steel, automatic, caliber AR 116, 24-hour indicator with rotating bezel under glass (second zone time), from 1975

Ebel
Sportwave Meridian, steel, automatic, Ebel caliber 122 (base ETA 2892-A2), 24-hour indicator (second zone time), from 1999

Ebel
Sportwave GMT, steel, automatic, Ebel caliber 123 (base ETA 2893-2), 24-hour indicator (second zone time), from 2006

Ebel
Voyager, steel, automatic, Ebel caliber 124 (base ETA 2892-A2), world time indicator, from 1999

Louis Erard
Power reserve/second time zone, steel, automatic, caliber ER 61, 24-hour indicator (second zone time), from 1999

Pilots' watches—with a difference

There can hardly be a professional group for whom it makes more sense to have a world time watch than pilots and other "frequent fliers" who incessantly cross the globe—which is why there is such a watch in the "Lufthansa Collection" of the Saxony-based German company Nautische Instrumente Mühle Glashütte. The most noticeable feature of this watch is an additional crown integrated into the lower strap holder of the stainless steel case. It serves to set the inner rotating bezel with the printed names of a place in each time zone. In this watch, the task of the rotating bezel with 24-hour divisions has been taken over by an orange lacquered pointer. Moving at half the speed of the hour hand, it brushes a delicate ring of figures printed on the black dial between the bezel with the names of cities and the minutes ring.

Eterna
KonTiki GMT, steel, automatic, ETA caliber 2893-2, 24-hour indicator (second zone time), from 2006

Formex
Diver GMT, steel/titanium, automatic, ETA caliber 2892-A2, 24-hour indicator (second zone time), water-resistant to 985 feet (300 m), from 2006

Fortis
Official Cosmonaut's Sport Pilot GMT, steel, automatic, ETA caliber 2893-2, 24-hour indicator (second zone time), from 1999

Fortis
Pilot Professional GMT, steel, automatic, ETA caliber 2893-2, 24-hour indicator (second zone time), from 1999

Fortis
Flieger GMT, steel, automatic, ETA caliber 2893-2, 24-hour indicator (second zone time), from 2006

Fortis
B-42 Official Cosmonaut's GMT, steel, automatic, ETA caliber 2893-2, 24-hour indicator (second zone time), from 2006

Fortis
B-42 Chrono GMT, ETA caliber 7750, 24-hour indicator (second zone time), chronograph, C.O.S.C. certified chronometer, from 2006

Below: Overview of world time zones

Gérald Genta
Night & Day, yellow gold, automatic, GG caliber 1961 (base ETA 2892-A2), second hour hand plus day/night indicator (second zone time), from 1999

207

Glycine
Airman 7, steel, automatic, three
independent ETA calibers, one with
additional 24-hour indicator (four
zone times), from 2006

Girard-Perregaux
GMT, white gold, GP caliber, separately adjustable second hour hand
(second zone time)

Girard-Perregaux
ww.tc Chronograph, white gold, automatic, GP caliber 3387,
24-hour indicator with bezel under glass (second zone time),
chronograph, from 2006

Girard-Perregaux
Vintage King Size Chrono GMT, rose gold, automatic, GP caliber
033C0, 24-hour indicator (second zone time), chronograph,
from 2006

Glycine
Airman 9, steel, automatic, ETA
caliber 7754, 24-hour indicator
(second zone time), chronograph,
from 2006

From Boston to Hamburg?
Press six times!

In 2000, Patek Philippe returned to the long tradition of the brand as a producer of world time watches, although this was a tradition they had not maintained for decades. Not least for that reason, Patek Philippe watches of this type sell today at auction for astronomical prices.

The new world time watch shows local time in all the world's 24 time zones at a glance and is distinguished by being particularly user-friendly: Two concentric rings turn about the central dial where minute and hour hands show local time. The inner ring has a 24-hour display

Heuer
Autavia GMT, steel, automatic, caliber 12, 24-hour indicator (second zone time), from 1975

Michel Herbelin
Newport J-Class GMT, steel, automatic, ETA caliber 2892 with module, 24-hour indicator (second zone time), power reserve indicator, from 2006

IWC
Aviator watch UTC, steel, automatic, IWC caliber C.37526, digital 24-hour indicator (second zone time), from 1999

Ikepod
Seaslug, steel, automatic, ETA caliber 2893-2, 24-hour indicator (second zone time), from 1999

209

Jaeger-LeCoultre
Reverso Géographique, steel,
automatic, JLC caliber 858, rotatable
city ring under glass on back of case
(world time), day/night indicator,
from 1999

Jaeger-LeCoultre
Reverso Grande GMT, steel, automatic, JLC caliber 878,
second time indicator plus day/night display on back
of case (second zone time), chronograph, from 2006

Jaeger-LeCoultre
Reverso Duoface, steel, automatic, JLC caliber 929/3,
second 12-hour indicator on back of case (second zone time),
from 1999

Jaeger-LeCoultre
Reverso Grande Automatique, steel,
automatic, JLC caliber 970,
adjustable second hour hand plus
day/night indicator (second zone
time), from 2006

Jaeger-LeCoultre
Master Geographic, red gold, automatic, JLC caliber 929/3,
rotatable city ring under glass on back of case (world time),
from 1999

Jaeger-LeCoultre
Master Geographic, steel, automatic, JLC caliber 929/3,
rotatable city ring under glass on back of case (world time),
from 1999

210

with day and night phases marked, while the outer ring is inscribed with 24 place names symbolizing the different time zones. These two rings can be used at any time to read the current time in the 24 time zones. In each case, the numbers "1" to "24" are positioned under a place name in the time zone concerned. The place and time with day/night display that can be seen above the pointer (shaped like an arrow) at the "12" correspond to the local time indicated by minute and hour hands.

Setting the watch is very easy. The user, for example, is in Paris at eight in the morning and wants to reset the watch. To do this, he or she

Jaeger-LeCoultre
Master Compressor Geographic, steel, automatic, JLC caliber 923, rotating city ring under glass plus AM/PM indicator (world time), from 2006

Jaeger-LeCoultre
Master Hometime, steel, automatic, JLC caliber 975, adjustable second hour hand plus day/night indicator (second zone time), from 2006

Jaeger-LeCoultre
Master Compressor Dualmatic, steel, automatic, JLC caliber 972, adjustable second hour hand plus 24-hour indicator (second zone time), from 2006

Jaeger-LeCoultre
Master Extreme World Chronograph, titanium, automatic, JLC caliber 923, rotating city bezel under glass plus AM/PM indicator (world time), chronograph, patented shock absorber system, from 2006

Kelek
Chronograph with second time zone, steel, automatic, Kelek caliber 7752, second separately adjustable hour hand (second zone time), from 1999

F.P. Journe
Chronomètre à Resonance, platinum, hand winding, F.P. Journe caliber 1499-2, second 12-hour indicator, from 2006

Kurth
Jubilee World Time Chrono No. 2, steel, automatic, ETA caliber 7750, rotating city ring under glass, chronograph, from 2006

presses the button on the left edge of the case at ten o'clock often enough to move Paris on to the 12 o'clock position. Then, as with every other watch, he or she sets the hands to eight o'clock using the winding crown. The whole 24-hour ring will now turn. The watch owner has to take care that the figure 8 (and not the 20) comes to be under the place name "Paris." Once this adjustment has been made, the crown is no longer used for adjustments.

Two days, two nights

It's not always necessary to make new discoveries from scratch to create something special. This has been proved again and again in recent years by the A. Lange & Söhne factory, which has demonstrated,

with impressive inventions, how everyday timepiece features such as a date display can be turned into technical treasures.

A world time watch is, of course, more complicated. After all, it is expected to display several zone times, preferably one for each of the 24 time zones. The Lange 1 Time Zone meets this demand in the classic manner, having a "city ring," the typical feature of a world time watch, around the edge of the main dial.

Two pairs of hands can be adjusted independently on the corresponding dials. According to the design principle on which Lange 1 is based, these are asymmetrically arranged. The display of the second zone time is on a subsidiary dial, with Arabic numbers,

Maurice Lacroix

Masterpiece Double Rétrograde, rose gold, hand winding, ML caliber 100 (base ETA 6498), digital second hour indicator (second zone time), from 1999

Maurice Lacroix

2ième Temps, steel/yellow gold, automatic, ML caliber 29 (base ETA 2836-2), 24-hour indicator (second zone time), retrograde date indicator, from 2006

Longines

Master Collection GMT, steel, automatic, Longines caliber L635 (base ETA 2824-2), 24-hour indicator (second zone time), from 2006

Minerva

Palladio Dual Time, steel, automatic, Minerva caliber 24 DT, 24-hour indicator, chronograph, from 1999

A. Lange & Söhne

Lange 1 Time Zone, red gold, hand winding, Lange caliber L031.1, rotating city bezel plus day/night indicator (world time), from 2006

Movado
Polygraph, steel, hand winding, 24-hour indicator (second zone time), from 1960

Montblanc
Masterpiece Dual Time, steel/gold, ETA caliber 2892-A2, 24-hour indicator (second zone time), from 1999

Montblanc
Time Walker GMT, steel, automatic, Montblanc caliber 4810/405 (base ETA 2893-2), 24-hour indicator (second zone time), from 2006

Franck Müller
Cintrée Curvex World Time, yellow gold, automatic, FM caliber 2800, 24-hour indicator (second zone time), from 1999

Mühle Glashütte
Traveler Automatic, steel, automatic, ETA caliber 2892-A2, 24-hour indicator (second zone time), from 1999

214

Franck Muller
Master Banker, steel, automatic,
FM caliber 2800, second 12-hour
indicator (second zone time),
from 1999

Franck Muller
Master Formula, steel,
automatic, FM caliber 7000
(base ETA 7750), 24-hour
indicator (second zone time),
chronograph, from 1999

Omega
Seamaster GMT, steel, automatic,
Omega caliber 1128 (base ETA
2892-A2), 24-hour indicator
(second zone time), C.O.S.C.
certified chronometer, from 1999

which has taken the position of the little seconds indicator dial in the Lange 1. The large subsidiary dial, with its gold Roman hour markings, provides the home time.

Each ring of figures has a day/night indicator, essential for time zone watches, added to it. Their tiny pointers run synchronously.

Two buttons for adjustment on the left of the case serve to set the large date and the individual world timepiece functions. Normally, when setting out on a journey, the city ring is set with the aid of the button at "8." This makes the ring inscribed with the names of 24 representative places in the individual time zones move round with each push—viewed geographically—one time zone further to the east. The hour hand of the subsidiary dial with the Arabic numbers also moves around correspondingly in this process, as does the day/night indicator.

Oris
Worldtimer, steel, automatic, Oris caliber 690 (base ETA 2836-2), second 12-hour indicator (second zone time), moon phase indicator, from 1999

Oris
Atelier Complication, steel, automatic, Oris caliber 4810/581 (base ETA 2688/2671), 24-hour indicator (second zone time), moon phase indicator, from 2006

Oris
Big Crown Complication, steel, automatic, Oris caliber 581 (base ETA 2688/2671), 24-hour indicator (second zone time), from 2006

Parmigiani
Toric Répétition Minutes GMT, rose gold, hand winding, Parmigiani caliber 251, 24-hour indicator (second zone time), quarter hour and minute repetition, from 2006

Of time zones and zone times

Our world is officially divided into 24 time zones, counting eastwards from the zero meridian. This is due to the east-west rotation of the Earth, which turns counterclockwise as seen from the North Pole and clockwise as seen from the South Pole. A world time watch can be set to each of the time zones. It cannot display the time zone itself, which is, after all, geographically defined and not a time term. It therefore displays the time of the zone of the Earth for which the watch has been set. The customary term of a watch with a "second time zone," often used in connection with GMT watches, is understandable therefore, but incorrect. To be correct, the reference when listing what a GMT or world time watch can show would have to be to a "second" or "third" "zone time."

Patek Philippe

World time watch, rose gold, automatic, Patek Philippe caliber 240 HU, two counter-rotating dials with world cities and 24-hour display (world time), from 2006

Patek Philippe

Calatrava Travel Time, yellow gold, hand winding, Patek Philippe caliber 215 PS FUS 24H, second, separately adjustable hour hand plus 24-hour indicator (second zone time), from 1999

Patek Philippe

Travel Time, yellow gold, hand winding, Patek Philippe caliber 215/156, second separately adjustable hour hand plus 24-hour indicator (second zone time), from 2006

Paul Picot

Gentleman Chrono GMT, steel, automatic, PP caliber 8104 (base ETA 7750), 24-hour indicator (second zone time), from 2006

From Ptolemy to UTC

Since ancient times there have been maps showing the Earth with its surface divided into a network of longitude and latitude. Ptolemy, when creating his maps, placed the zero meridian in the region of the Canary Islands (today some 15 degrees west longitude). Later cartographers moved the zero meridian to Rome, Copenhagen, Paris, or St. Petersburg, before it was finally "moved" to London. As the Earth turns on its own axis, and every meridian makes a line between the North and South Poles, the position of the zero meridian is in fact of no importance and was purely a political matter.

Auguste Reymond
Cotton Club Global Time, steel, automatic, ETA caliber 2893-2, 24-hour indicator (second zone time), from 1999

Rolex
GMT Master, steel, automatic, Rolex caliber 1030, 24-hour hand (second zone time), adjustable bezel with 24 divisions, C.O.S.C. certified chronometer, from 1956

Rolex
GMT Master, steel, automatic, Rolex caliber 3175 (base Rolex 3135), 24-hour hand (second zone time), adjustable bezel with 24 divisions, C.O.S.C. certified chronometer, from 1999

Rolex
Explorer, steel, automatic, Rolex caliber 3185 (base Rolex 3135), 24-hour hand (second zone time), C.O.S.C. certified chronometer, from 1999

Rolex

GMT Master II, yellow gold, automatic, Rolex caliber 3185 (base Rolex 3135), 24-hour hand (second zone time), adjustable bezel with 24 divisions, C.O.S.C. certified chronometer, from 2006

Daniel Roth

GMT, steel, automatic, modified GP caliber 3100, second digital hour indicator (second zone time), from 1999

Schwarz Etienne

Chronograph GMT, steel, automatic, LIP caliber 8104 (base ETA 7750), 24-hour indicator (second zone time) chronograph, from 2006

Schwarz Etienne

Carée, automatic, LIP caliber 8154 (base ETA 7750), 24-hour indicator (second zone time), chronograph, from 2006

219

Sinn

Multifunction Chronograph, steel, automatic, modified ETA caliber 7750, 24-hour indicator (second zone time), chronograph, from 2006

Sinn

Aviator with magnetic field protection and second time zone, surface hardened steel, automatic, ETA caliber 2893-2, 24-hour display (second zone time), from 2006

Sinn

Frankfurt World Time, steel, automatic, modified ETA caliber 2893-2, 24-hour indicator (second zone time), rotating bezel with 12 divisions under glass (third zone time), from 2006

Sinn

World Time Chronograph, steel, automatic, modified ETA caliber 7750, 24-hour indicator (second zone time), chronograph, from 1999

Seen against the background of how easily the expressions "time zone" and "zone time" can lead to misunderstandings, it is not hard to imagine the difficulties connected to the introduction of these terms.

The problems began with the dispute between those eternal rivals, Great Britain and France, about determining the zero meridian. The one party naturally wanted it in London and the other, of course, in Paris. After the Royal Observatory in the London suburb of Greenwich published a Nautical Almanac (in 1767), the

TAG Heuer
Carrera Twin-Time, steel, automatic, TAG Heuer caliber 7 (base ETA 2893-2), 24-hour indicator (second time zone), from 2006

Sothis
World Time Chrono, steel, automatic, modified ETA caliber 7750, reference cities for time zones on the bezel under glass, from 1999

Temption
Automat with second time zone, steel, automatic, ETA caliber 2893-2, 24-hour indicator (second zone time), from 1999

Tiffany
Streamamerica World Time, steel, automatic, ETA caliber, 2824-2, world time indicator, from 1999

Tiffany
Classic Two Time Tonneau, steel, quartz-controlled, ETA caliber 280.002, second 12-hour indicator, from 1999

Tutima
Aviator Chronograph F2 UTC, steel,
automatic, modified ETA caliber
7750, 24-hour indicator (second
zone time), chronograph, from 2006

Tissot
Navigator Seastar T12, steel,
automatic, caliber 798, 24-hour dial,
rotating bezel under glass with names
of reference cities for time zones
(world time indicator), from 1975

Tutima
Automatic FX UTC, steel, automatic,
ETA caliber 2893-2, 24-hour indicator
(second zone time), from 2006

confident Anglo-Saxons ruled that the zero meridian, the determining line for worldwide timekeeping, should run through the English capital. From then on, people spoke of "Greenwich Mean Time" (GMT).

Countries spread out over a long distance east to west, such as Russia or the USA, naturally had the most problems with the many different local times (there were more than 300!). This might well be the reason why it was the American Meteorological Society that, in 1875, provided the impetus for creating a uniform time system valid worldwide, which was agreed upon in 1884. The division of the Earth into 24 time zones followed. There was a difference of one hour from one time zone to the next, increasing as you moved from west to east and based on the zero meridian. Gradually, every country joined this system. Even France eventually accepted London as the site of zero longitude.

Since the day has 24 hours in which the world turns once, that is to say, describes a full circle of 360 degrees, a time zone covers 15 degrees of longitude (360 degrees divided by 24 = 15 degrees)—in theory.

In practice, there are considerably more time zones, for geographic and political reasons, because some countries want to have half-hourly divisions between time zones, or have only one time zone—such as in China—although they are gigantic countries. In addition, many countries do not use summer time, which would, in any case, make little sense in countries near to the equator, which have almost equal phases of light and dark.

Central European Time (CET) was introduced in 1893 and corresponds to Greenwich time plus one hour. This time zone stretches from the western shores of Spain to the eastern borders of Poland, covering a stretch of nearly 35 degrees longitude.

Ulysse Nardin
Perpetual Calendar GMT +/−, white gold, automatic, UN caliber 32, 24-hour hand (second zone time), perpetual calendar, from 2006

Ulysse Nardin
San Marco GMT +/−, steel, automatic, UN caliber 20, 24-hour indicator (second zone time), perpetual calendar, from 1999

Ulysse Nardin
GMT +/−, Big Date Dual Time, red gold, automatic, UN caliber 22, digital 24-hour indicator (second zone time), perpetual calendar, from 2006

Universal Genève
Janus, platinum/red gold, hand winding, Universal Genève caliber 42, double hour display plus day/night indicator (second zone time), reversible case, from 1999

223

Victorinox

AirBoss Mach 5, steel, automatic, ETA caliber 2893-2, 24-hour indicator (second zone time), from 2006

Vulcain

Aviator GMT, steel, hand winding, Vulcain caliber V-10, 24-hour indicator (second zone time), alarm function, from 2006

Vacheron Constantin

Royal Eagle Dual Time, white gold, automatic, Vacheron Constantin caliber 1222 H393, second 12-hour indicator plus day/night indicator (second zone time), from 2006

Vacheron Constantin

Malte Dual Time, rose gold, Vacheron Constantin caliber 1206 RDT, 24-hour indicator (second zone time), C.O.S.C. certified chronometer, from 2006

Since 1972 the International Telecommunication Union has used the abbreviation UTC, a compromise between CUT (Coordinated Universal Time) used by English speakers and TUC (*Temps Universel Coordonné*) used by French speakers. UTC has uniform seconds defined by International Atomic Time, with leap seconds introduced irregularly to compensate for discrepancies. UTC, used for atomic clocks, broadcast by short wave radios and via satellite, is also oriented to the zero meridian, but instead of using Anglo-Saxon descriptions such as "5 a.m." for the morning and "5 p.m." for the afternoon, time is given unambiguously in 24-hour notation. The four-digit form is used both in writing and when giving the spoken time. For example, one o'clock in the morning is UTC 0100; when spoken, it is "zero one hundred."

George J. von Burg
GMT Flyback, steel automatic, GJVB caliber 8107 (base ETA 7750), 24-hour indicator (second zone time), chronograph with Flyback function, from 2006

Raymond Weil
Don Giovanni Cosi Grande Two Time Zones, steel, automatic, RW caliber 2200 (base ETA 2671), 24-hour indicator (second zone time), from 2006

Zenith
Grande Class Power Reserve Dual Time, rose gold, automatic, Zenith caliber 683 Elite, 24-hour indicator (second zone time), power reserve display, from 2006

Zenith
Class Dual Time, steel, automatic, Zenith caliber 682 Elite, 24-hour indicator (second zone time), from 2006

Harry Winston
Greenwich, yellow gold, automatic, second hour hand plus day/night indicator (second zone time), from 1999

225

6. WATCHES WITH ALARM FEATURES

Watches with alarm features were always exotic items, although today, when cheap digital watches and mobile phones have alarm functions, they are really only of interest to watch-lovers with a liking for extravagance.

Breguet
Alarm watch, Le Réveil du Tsar, yellow gold, automatic, Breguet caliber 519 F, automatic winding of the alarm movement, 24-hour indicator (second zone time), from 2006

Certina
Alarm, steel, automatic, caliber AS 5007, from 1976

Cyma
Time-o-Vox, steel/gold-plated, hand winding, Cyma caliber 464, from 1953

Cartier
Alarm watch, steel, hand winding, JLC caliber 489/1, from 1952

The few watches still on offer today with this delightful additional function usually have a type of movement devised back in the 1940s and 50s. New designs of alarm watches are rare. In the way they work, these small alarms have a good deal in common with their fat tin relatives—the ones that in years gone by stood on many bedside tables and ticked so loudly it was difficult to get the sleep from which they were intended to wake you the following morning. It is of course one advantage of an alarm on your wrist that you can only hear it when it is intended to wake you.

Let's look at the function first. Under the hour wheel (to which the hour hand is attached) there is a leaf spring fastened to one end of the bottom plate. It covers the whole of this and protrudes into the movement on the other side. There are two cams on the hour wheel. The leaf spring forms a ring enclosing the set-hands arbor and from below gently presses the hour wheel in the direction of the dial. There is the alarm-set wheel, which can only be adjusted

from outside via the crown, and which has two small notches into which the hour wheel with its cams can fit if the hour wheel and the alarm-set wheel are in a particular relationship to one another. This point in time is the alarm time.

When the cams of the hour wheel slot into the notches in the alarm-set wheel, this moves the free end of the leaf spring slightly and thus releases the alarm hammer, previously blocked by the leaf spring. The hammer then strikes quickly against the back of the case or some other resonant body, making a rattling noise or a delicate ringing, and vibrating the watch on the wrist.

A watch that lets its voice be heard

When watch-lovers talk about alarm wristwatches, they often mention Memovox. This is the name of the alarm by Jaeger-LeCoultre, which has been part of their range—constantly being updated—since 1951. The name says it all, deriving as it does from the Latin words

Eterna
1948 alarm, steel, automatic, base AS 5008, replica of the first Eterna-Matic, from 2006

Fortis
Manager, steel, hand winding, AS caliber 1475, from 1954

Dubey & Schaldenbrand
Steel, automatic, LIP caliber 5900 (base AS 5008), 24-hour indicator (second zone time), from 2006

Fortis
B-42 Official Cosmonaut's Chrono Alarm, steel, automatic, Fortis caliber (base ETA 7750), chronograph, alarm movement with automatic winding, 24-hour indicator (second zone time), from 2006

IWC
GST Automatic Alarm, titanium, automatic, IWC caliber C.197, from 1999

229

Jaeger-LeCoultre
LeCoultre Wrist Alarm, steel/gold-plated, hand winding, caliber JLC 814, from 1951

Jaeger-LeCoultre
Memovox, steel, hand winding, caliber JLC 489/1, from 1951

Jaeger-LeCoultre
Memovox Automatic, steel, automatic, caliber JLC 916, from 1951

Jaeger-LeCoultre
Master Memovox, red gold, automatic, JLC 914, perpetual calendar with double moon phase display, from 2006

memorare (to remember) and *vox* (voice). The first Memovox watches raised their voices by having the rapidly moving hammer strike a pin that protruded into the movement from the inner side of the case back and made a rasping sound.

Today, several generations of watches later, the Memovox produces a restrained, dulcet ring. This comes from a semicircular gong which is screwed into the back and thus uses the whole case as a resonating body. While the movement is automatically wound by a rotor, the wearer has to wind the alarm movement by hand. For winding and setting the alarm, all Memovox versions use the crown at two o'clock.

Vulcain's Crickets

The second classic among wristwatch alarms is Vulcain's Cricket. It owes its name to the scraping and chirping sound made by crickets—unpleasant to some ears. Hearers are reminded of it as soon as the Cricket rings. This wristwatch

Junghans
Minivox, steel, hand winding,
Junghans caliber 89, from 1960

Jaeger-LeCoultre
Master Grand Réveil, platinum, automatic
JLC 909/1, from 1999

Jaeger-LeCoultre
Master Compressor Memovox, steel,
automatic JLC 918 (base JLC 916),
bidirectional rotating bezel under glass,
compressor crown seal system, from 2006

alarm was developed in 1947 by Robert Ditisheim, former boss of the Swiss watch company, Vulcain. His greatest concern was that the alarm was not loud enough. His friend, a professor of physics, Paul Langevinb, made the helpful suggestion of using a little bell made of beryllium bronze to solve the problem.

"My father had been working on this problem for seven years," Robert Ditisheim's son, Michael, later said, describing these efforts. Since then, a resonance space has been added under the outer case lid, separated by a second back. The alarm hammer now strikes the anvil of this inner back and truly does make enough noise to wake you up. The double-walled case back remains a special feature of the Vulcain wristwatch alarm to this day. It is also worth mentioning the clever yet simple operation of the Cricket. The time is set quite normally by pulling out the crown, which is then pushed in again. To set the alarm movement, you press the button at two o'clock. The crown will jump out again and the alarm time can then be set.

Maurice Lacroix
Masterpiece Réveil Globe, steel,
automatic, ML caliber 06 (base
AS 5008), bidirectional rotating
bezel under glass, from 2006

Jaeger-LeCoultre
AMVOX 1 Alarm, steel, automatic JLC 918 (base JLC 916),
result of cooperation with the sports car company Aston
Martin, from 2006

231

Lémania
Wristwatch alarm, steel, automatic,
Lémania caliber LWO 2980,
from 1971

Omega
Seamaster Memomatic, steel,
automatic, caliber 980, from 1971

The button also serves to shorten the alarm sound if required.

Apart from Vulcain, only Jaeger-LeCoultre offered one particular quality: the alarm movement built into a diver's watch. Divers can therefore receive an acoustic warning of the time to resurface. The diver can also read the decompression times required off the dial. In 1961, a Swiss diving pioneer achieved a depth record, in a lake, of 728 feet (222 meters), wearing a Vulcain Cricket Nautical.

Péquignet
Mooréa Réveil, steel, automatic,
caliber AS 5008, from 1999

Nivrel
Alarm, steel, automatic, caliber
AS 5008, from 1999

Revue Thommen
Cricket, 1997, steel, hand winding,
Revue Thommen caliber RT 80,
from 1999

Pierce
Alarm, steel, automatic, alarm,
AS caliber 5008, from 1976

Sinn
Frankfurt Financial District Alarm, steel,
automatic, AS caliber 5008, automatic
winding for alarm movement, 24-hour
indicator (second zone time), bidirectional
rotating bezel under glass, from 2006

Tiffany
Classic Alarm, steel, quartz, ETA caliber
926.301, from 1999

The ideal traveling alarm

Two complications in one watch are not in fact
all that rare, but combining an alarm with a
time zone watch is a good idea. On journeys in
particular, a wristwatch alarm is of practical
use. A model example is the Blancpain Léman
Réveil GMT. This has a movement of more
than 400 individual parts, with an automatic
winding action providing power for both the
running and the alarm movements. This watch
is very easy to operate. The time and the second
zone time are set by the crown at the two
o'clock position, the alarm time by means of a
second crown at the four. The alarm is switched
on and off by means of a button at the eight.
The status quo (on or off) can be seen on the
dial. The alarm function is controlled by a
classic column wheel, and its hammers strike

Auguste Reymond
Rumba Alarm, steel, automatic,
AS caliber 5008, automatic winding
for alarm movement, from 2006

233

Vulcain
Cricket, red gold, hand winding,
Vulcain caliber 120, from 1960

Vulcain
Cricket Calendar, steel/gold-plated,
hand winding, Vulcain caliber 401,
from 1954

Ulysse Nardin
Sonata, red gold, automatic, Ulysse Nardin
caliber UN 66, alarm with precise
adjustment to the minute, 24-hour indicator
(second zone time), from 2006

Louis Vuitton
Tambour Réveil Automatique, steel,
automatic, LV caliber 113 (base AS caliber
5008), automatic winding of alarm
movement, 24-hour indicator (second zone
time), from 2006

Ulysse Nardin
San Marco Alarm, automatic, Ulysse Nardin
caliber UN 60, from 1999

a gong such as is found in repeater watches. This watch alarm sounds just as melodious.

Ulysse Nardin has achieved a comparable effect with the Sonata. It owes its name to the melodic sound of its alarm, created by a gong made of hardened steel. Screwed down at one end only, it is wound around the movement and can therefore be set into a marked oscillating motion by the alarm hammer. Special features of the Sonata are that the alarm time can be set to the exact minute and the zone time can be effortlessly adjusted by a plus and a minus button.

Vulcain
Cricket Nautical, steel, hand winding, Vulcain caliber 120, with diver's decompression table on the dial, from 1961

Vulcain
Lady Millésime 1928, steel, hand winding, Vulcain caliber V-11, from 2006

Vulcain
Aviator Elapse Time, steel, hand winding, Vulcain caliber V-11, from 2006

Vulcain
Aviator Dual-Time, steel, hand winding, Vulcain caliber V-12, additional 12-hour indicator (second zone time), from 2006

7. TOURBILLON WATCHES

The basic idea of the tourbillon is as simple as it is ingenious. If a watch in a vertical position is allowed to rotate slowly but constantly around the arbor of the hands, all errors of the escapement regulator will have been corrected after each revolution. However, it is hardly practical to allow the whole watch to rotate. Breguet therefore concentrated on the regulator and devised a mechanism that ensured that the entire escapement within the movement rotated around its own arbor. The design and construction of a tourbillon are still considered the crown of watchmaking skill today—and they are correspondingly expensive.

Audemars Piguet
Tourbillon II, yellow gold, automatic, AP caliber 2875, power reserve indicator, from 1999

Arnold & Son
Tourbillon, white gold, automatic, A & S caliber 1805, from 2006

Audemars Piguet
Edward Piguet Tourbillon large date, white gold, hand winding, AP caliber 2874, from 2006

Clockmaking in the eighteenth century was characterized more than ever before by concerted efforts to force mechanical timepieces to the outermost limits of accuracy. For navigation at sea, the exact time had become an absolutely vital factor. The hunt for a clock that kept the exact time reached its climax with a prize for solving the longitude problem offered by the British Parliament in 1714. In 1773, after lengthy discussions, the prize of £20,000 went to the English clockmaker John Harrison (1693–1776). From that point on, large numbers of ships' chronometers were built, becoming ever better in performance. Although these timepieces were of modest sizes compared to the other navigation instruments used onboard ship, they were quite unsuitable for use on land, being far too big and sensitive. Many clockmakers therefore found a new challenge in the optimization of travel clocks and watches.

The biggest problem for precision clockmakers lay in the various awkward qualities of the metals available at the time. It seemed impossible to solve. At different temperatures metals change their physical qualities and their dimensional accuracy. The escapement assembly, composed of the balance wheel and balance spring, was particularly badly affected. The steel spiral was sensitive to temperature changes, which changed the spiral's elasticity. Increases in temperature would make the spring's power slacken, leading to the watch becoming slow. If, on the other hand, the watch were allowed get cold, it would run faster, due to the growing elasticity of the balance spring.

Blancpain
Villeret Tourbillon power reserve,
platinum, automatic, Blancpain
caliber 25, from 2006

Audemars Piguet
Tourbillon III, platinum, hand winding, AP caliber
2871, from 1999

Blancpain
Léman Tourbillon large date, red gold, automatic,
Blancpain caliber 6925, from 2006

Blancpain
Léman Tourbillon large date,
platinum, automatic, Blancpain
caliber 6925, transparent dial,
from 2006

Blancpain
Le Brassus Chronograph Flyback
Ratrappante with tourbillon, red gold,
automatic, Blancpain caliber 56F9U,
from 2006

239

Breguet
Tourbillon with power reserve, yellow gold, hand winding, Breguet caliber 560T, power reserve indicator, from 1999

Breguet
Tourbillon, yellow gold, hand winding, Breguet caliber 558T, from 1999

Breguet
Tourbillon Perpetual Calendar, yellow gold, hand winding, Breguet caliber 558QPT, from 1999

Breguet
Tourbillon with power reserve indicator, platinum, hand winding, Breguet caliber 560T, retrograde 24-hour indicator, from 2006

Breguet
Grande Complication Tourbillon avec Réserve de Marche, yellow gold, automatic, Breguet caliber 587DR, from 2006

Breguet
Tourbillon with perpetual calendar, hand winding, Breguet caliber 558QPSQ, skeleton hand-engraved movement, from 2006

Error compensation

While clockmakers such as John Harrison and Thomas Earnshaw attempted to correct the error on the balance spring itself, Pierre Le Roy in Paris had the idea of developing a special balance wheel that would compensate for errors. The principle underlying the self-compensating balance wheel was already known from the construction of thermometers and is based on the fact that different metals expand at different rates when temperatures rise. If two metal strips with different expansion coefficients are inseparably linked, for instance, by being rolled together, the result is a so-called bimetallic strip, which bends of its own accord when the temperature changes, because both metals expand at different rates. The ring of a self-compensating balance wheel is, depending on

the design, broken in two or three places, and is made from a bent bimetallic strip. With a two-arm self-compensating balance, the two segments of the wheel each have one end fastened to the arm. The other end is free and can therefore follow the expansion of the metal. The outer strip of the split wheel consists of the metal with the higher expansion coefficient (generally brass); the inner, like the arms, is of steel.

When the temperature rises, the brass expands and presses the free ends of the ring inwards, thus making the balance wheel smaller. The moment of inertia of the balance wheel is lowered, and it begins to oscillate faster. However, as the elasticity constant of the balance spring lessens when warmed, and this then makes the balance wheel run more slowly, the two errors balance each other out to a

Bulgari
Tourbillon, yellow gold, hand winding, Bulgari caliber MVT 9902 TB (base GP caliber 9902), power reserve indicator at the back of the movement, from 1999

Bulgari
Bulgari Tourbillon, yellow gold, hand winding, Daniel Roth caliber R&G 052, power reserve indicator at back of movement, from 2006

Bulgari
Rettangolo Tourbillon, platinum, hand winding, Claret caliber 97, 100 hours' power reserve, limited edition of 20 timepieces, from 2006

241

Philippe Charriol
Celtic Le Tourbillon, yellow gold,
hand winding, Renaud & Papi caliber,
from 1999

Chopard
L.U.C. 4T Quattro Tourbillon, red gold, hand winding, L.U.C.
caliber 1.02, four spring barrels, over 200 hours' power reserve,
C.O.S.C. certified chronometer, from 2006

Chopard
L.U.C. Steel Wings Tourbillon, platinum, hand winding,
L.U.C. caliber 4TB, over 200 hours' power reserve,
C.O.S.C. certified chronometer, from 2006

Corum
Tourbillon Mystérieuse, yellow gold,
hand winding, developed exclusively
for Corum by Christopher Claret,
transparent bottom plates and
sapphire bridges, from 1999

Chronoswiss
Régulateur à Tourbillon
Squelette, white gold,
hand winding,
Chronoswiss caliber
C.361 (base STT),
cantilevered minute
tourbillon, two spring
barrels, from 2006

certain extent. How difficult it is to correct one error by means of another, watchmakers had to discover in practice, for what looks all right in a calculation will in reality often behave quite differently from the way it was worked out on paper. To take care of the fine-tuning, self-compensating balance wheels are provided with numerous threaded holes for the attachment of various adjusting and weighting screws, which can influence, among other things, the extent of the compensation.

Mobility creates new problems

As could have been expected, compensating for so-called temperature errors paved the way for

plenty of other potential errors no one had previously thought of. The fact that the bimetallic strips that made the balance wheel rings did not behave as one would have wished was particularly annoying. After a change in temperature, they did not return to their original conditions, and also, due to a lack of precision in manufacturing, they did not behave symmetrically. This meant that the center of gravity of the entire escapement was constantly on the move and only very rarely exactly within the axis of the balance wheel.

This was not so very important where ships' chronometers were concerned, as the balance wheel was always oscillating in a horizontal

Roger Dubuis
Sympathie Tourbillon, white gold, hand winding, RD caliber 1102, perpetual calendar, limited edition of 28, from 2006

Roger Dubuis
Golden Square Flying Tourbillon, rose gold, hand winding, RD caliber 03, crown push button to correct date, limited edition of 28, from 2006

De Witt
Académia Tourbillon Différentiel, titanium/red gold, hand winding, De Witt caliber DW 8002, cantilevered minute tourbillon, 110 hours' power reserve, from 2006

Gérald Genta
Octo Tourbillon Incontro, platinum, automatic, Gérald Genta caliber 9051, retrograde hour display, quartz movement with digital display on the back of the case including alarm, chronograph, and calendar, from 2006

243

plane. For pocket watches, on the other hand, obvious variations in the movement in various vertical positions were most irritatingly evident.

Yet another new invention

On December 23, 1800—the Republican Calendar of revolutionary France had the date Nivose 3, year IX—Breguet sent a note to the Minister of the Interior: "I am honored to submit to you a *mémoire* with a description of an invention that can be applied to timepieces, and which I would like to name '*Régulateur à Tourbillon*,' and also request the privilege of being the sole individual permitted to construct such regulators for ten years."

Breguet subsequently described his *régulateur* as being in a position "to annul the anomalies caused by the various positions of the center of

Girard-Perregaux
Tourbillon Président, yellow gold, hand winding, GP caliber 9800, minute tourbillon on the back of the movement, from 1999

Girard-Perregaux
Tourbillon with three gold bridges, platinum, GP caliber 9600, minute tourbillon, movement cut to skeleton form and engraved by hand, from 1999

Girard-Perregaux
Tourbillon ww.tc, rose gold, hand winding, GP caliber 098G0, minute tourbillon on the back of the works, 24-hour indicator (world time), from 2006

Girard-Perregaux
Vintage Tourbillon with three gold bridges, red gold, automatic, GP caliber 9600C, minute tourbillon, micro-rotor, from 2006

Girard-Perregaux
Vintage Tourbillon with gold bridge, red gold, automatic, GP caliber 9610C, minute tourbillon, micro-rotor, from 2006

gravity of the escapements." A few months later, on June 26, 1801 (or Messidor 7, year IX), Breguet received the desired patent, giving him the exclusive right for ten years to be the sole individual producing such tourbillons. The first watch with a *régulateur à tourbillon* was sold in 1805. A mere 35 such watches were sold in Breguet's lifetime.

It was typical of Breguet's sense of self-advertisement and what we would nowadays call "marketing" that he immediately gave his invention an appropriate name. "Tourbillon" means whirlwind, yet in the 1772 *Encyclopedia* of Diderot and d'Alembert the word is also used, in analogy with Descartes' *Principes*, to refer to the momentum that keeps the planets rotating about the sun; in other words, a very even motion. Many other terms, such as "rotational motion,"

Glashütte Original
Alfred Hellwig Tourbillon, rose gold, hand winding, Glashütte Original caliber 41, cantilevered minute tourbillon, from 1999

Glashütte Original
Julius Assmann Tourbillon, rose gold, hand winding, Glashütte Original caliber 51, cantilevered minute tourbillon on back of works, perpetual calendar, from 1999

Hublot
Big Bang Tourbillon, steel, hand winding, cantilevered minute tourbillon, limited edition of nine, from 2006

Glashütte Original
PanoMatic Tourbillon, rose gold, automatic, Glashütte Original caliber 93, cantilevered minute tourbillon, limited edition of 100, from 2006

Jaeger-LeCoultre

Master Gyrotourbillon, platinum, hand winding, JLC caliber 177, spherical tourbillon with two rotating arbors, direct display of equation of time, perpetual calendar, limited edition of 75, from 2006

F.P. Journe

Tourbillon Souverain à seconde morte, platinum, hand winding, escapement with seconde morte, cantilevered minute tourbillon, power reserve indicator, from 2006

have been used in an attempt to give the movement another name, but without a chance of success.

The trick with the turn

The basic idea of the tourbillon is as simple as it is ingenious. If a pocket watch is allowed to rotate in a vertical position slowly but steadily around the arbor of the hands, all errors in the center of gravity of the escapement would necessarily be corrected after each rotation. It is, of course, hardly practical to rotate the whole watch. Breguet therefore concentrated on the escapement regulator and devised a mechanism to ensure that the entire escapement assembly rotated within the movement on its own arbor.

The technical drawings show a little cage of steel, physically attached in a rotatable position to the main plate. The rotatable cage is moved by the third wheel across a pinion

Daniel JeanRichard

TV Screen Tourbillon, platinum, automatic, JR caliber (base Girard-Perregaux), from 2006

A. Lange & Söhne

Tourbillon pour le Mérité, yellow gold, hand winding, Lange caliber L.902.0, driving power regulated via chain and fusée plus stepped and planetary gear, from 1999 riveted to the arbor. It is situated, therefore, in the place where the second hand is normally to be found. For watches with anchor escapements, the balance wheel, anchor and escapement are arranged on a little platform in the center of the tourbillon cage, with the balance wheel generally being in the middle and turning on its own arbor. On the arbor of the escapement wheel there is a pinion, engaging through the floor of the cage with a fixed cogwheel fastened to the plate. While the third wheel sets the cage rotating, this rotation is braked once more by the escapement wheel pinion engaging with the fixed cogwheel.

The rotational movement of the cage can be set at different speeds. In modern watches, tourbillons perform a full rotation about once

Richard Mille
Tourbillon RM 002-V2, red gold, hand winding, RM caliber 002-V2, bottom plate made from carbon fiber, from 2006

Movado
Museum Tourbillon, platinum, hand winding, minute tourbillon on the back of the movement, individual piece, from 2006

Franck Muller
Cintrée Curvex Tourbillon Imperiale, yellow gold, hand winding, FM caliber TFM95, from 1999

Franck Muller
Long Island Tourbillon, white gold, hand winding, FM caliber 2001, from 2006

Richard Mille
Tourbillon RM 009 Felipe Massa, aluminum-silicon carbide, hand winding, RM caliber 009 FM, special series to honor the Brazilian Formula 1 racing driver Felipe Massa, limited edition of 25, from 2006

247

Parmigiani
Kalpa XL Tourbillon, rose gold, hand winding, Parmigiani caliber 500, 30-second tourbillon, from 2006

Patek Philippe
10 Jours Tourbillon, platinum, hand winding, Patek Philippe caliber 28-20REC10 PS IRM, minute tourbillon on the back of the movement, ten-day power reserve, C.O.S.C. certified chronometer, from 2006

Piaget
Emperador Tourbillon, rose gold, hand winding, Piaget caliber 600P, cantilevered minute tourbillon, from 2006

Robergé
Andromède II Tourbillon, white gold, hand winding, base caliber Lémania 387, from 1999

Daniel Roth
Tourbillon Double Face, yellow gold, hand winding, base caliber Lémania 2187, date and power reserve indicators on the back of the movement, from 1999

Daniel Roth
Tourbillon 200 Hours Power Reserve, rose gold, hand winding, Daniel Roth caliber DR 720, date and power reserve indicator on the back of the movement, from 2006

a minute. This makes it possible to mount the second hand directly onto the cage arbor. Breguet's first tourbillons were also minute tourbillons. He did experiment later with tourbillon cages that rotated once on their own arbor in four or even six minutes, but kept coming back to the minute tourbillon.

Breguet's tourbillon did indeed help the pocket watch to maintain even greater precision, but for him that seemed to have been more of a pleasant side effect. The essential point for him

and for his reputation was the fact the he had once again devised a mechanism that could not be so quickly copied by anyone else. Tourbillon watches were bought, then as now, mainly by wealthy people who were less interested in the precise time than in the exclusive nature of this little technical gem. As a tourbillon in a watch fulfills no visible additional function that can be proudly shown off, it was not long before the first watches with pierced dials were made, allowing observers to see the mechanism at work.

Alain Silberstein
Tourbillon Kronomarine, steel, hand winding, base caliber Lémania 2387, minute tourbillon, limited edition of ten, from 1999

Alain Silberstein
Tourbillon Emaille Dragon, yellow gold, hand winding, base caliber Lémania LWO 387, minute tourbillon, enamel dial in cloisonné technique, limited edition of ten, from 1999

Alain Silberstein
Tourbillon African Summer, steel, hand winding, ASC caliber 1.1 (base STT), minute tourbillon, limited edition of 500, from 2006

Alain Silberstein
Tourbillon Emaille Squelette, sapphire/titanium, hand winding, base caliber Lémania LWO 8701, minute tourbillon, limited edition of ten, from 1999

Vacheron Constantin
Les Complications Tourbillon,
yellow gold, hand winding,
Vacheron Constantin caliber 2250,
four spring barrels, 250 hours' power
reserve, double power reserve
indicator, from 2006

Ulysse Nardin
Royal Blue Tourbillon, platinum, hand winding, Ulysse Nardin
caliber UN 74, flying minute tourbillon, from 2005

Ulysse Nardin
Freak, white gold, hand winding, Ulysse Nardin caliber UN 01,
carousel tourbillon with patented Dual-Ulysse escapement,
parts of the movement act as hands, from 2005

Union
Johannes Dürrstein 3, rose
gold, hand winding, Union
caliber 45-01, flying minute
tourbillon, from 2005

Vacheron Constantin
Saint-Gervais, platinum, hand
winding, Vacheron Constantin caliber
1760, two spring barrels, power
reserve indicator, from 1999

Harry Winston
Excenter Tourbillon, platinum,
hand winding, HW caliber 400A,
from 2006

Louis Vuitton
Tourbillon Tambour Monogram, white gold, hand winding,
third wheel can be customized as desired (e.g. as a monogram),
from 2006

Exclusivity is the answer

It is still extremely difficult today to make a tourbillon. Apart from the fact that it is supposed to look fascinatingly delicate and filigreed, a tourbillon is, of course, mainly intended to improve the running of a watch. The complicated mechanism, however, is in exactly the place where the movement has the least power. The drive that the second wheel can impart to the escapement is some 300 times weaker than on the teeth of the spring barrel. Friction in this part of the watch must therefore be as low as possible. If the whole mechanism is then supposed to rotate, it must also be as light and filigreed as possible. For this reason, it is a very special challenge for a clock designer and clockmaker to construct a functioning tourbillon that also demonstrates better running values than the ordinary pendulum. It is even more difficult to miniaturize the whole thing so that it fits into a wristwatch.

Vulcain
Tourbillon Imperial Gong, rose gold, hand winding,
Vulcan caliber V-30, cantilevered minute tourbillon,
alarm signal on two gongs, from 2006

Zenith
Chronomaster XXT Tourbillon, rose gold, automatic,
Zenith caliber 4005 El Primero, minute tourbillon,
chronograph, 2006

Harry Winston
Tourbillon, platinum, hand winding,
from 2006

8. CALENDAR WATCHES

A useful additional function of a watch, even in the electronic age, is undoubtedly an indication of the date. Things are made even easier for the wearer if the watch also shows the day of the week, the month, and even the year. The gold standard in this category of watches is the perpetual calendar, which even leap years cannot throw off course.

Angelus
Chronodato, steel/gold-plated,
hand winding, full calendar,
chronograph, from 1948

Audemars Piguet
Royal Oak Offshore, yellow gold,
automatic, AP caliber 2120 QP,
full calendar, from 1999

Audemars Piguet
Royal Oak Quantième Perpétuel,
yellow gold, automatic, AP caliber
2120 QP, perpetual calendar,
from 1999

Audemars Piguet
Quantième Perpétuel Jubilee Model,
red gold, automatic, AP caliber
2120 QP, perpetual calendar,
from 1999

Audemars Piguet
Millenary Quantième Perpétuel, yellow
gold, automatic, AP caliber 2120 QP,
perpetual calendar, from 1999

254

Date indicators were among the earliest additional displays for mechanical clocks. For the standard date indicator on wristwatches, there is a train on the side of the base plate facing the dial and, depending upon the design, perhaps a few levers and a ratchet. One of the wheels of the train engages with the hour wheel, which carries the hour hand, and is driven by it. The date control system moves continuously along with the hands and changes the date, either slowly over several hours or suddenly with a jerk at midnight. This is done by a ring of fine brass plate, more rarely of plastic, placed at the outer edge of the movement plate. The ring bears the numbers "1" to "31" and has a toothed inner ring. Engaging with this ring is an attachment placed on a wheel controlled by the movement. The ratchet mentioned above serves to keep the date ring at rest after the switch-over, maintaining the current date exactly under the date window in the dial, even when the watch is moved.

The basic principle has been improved upon in many ways by watch designers. The so-called quick switch, for example, moves the date on by one day at midnight exactly using a spring tightened for several hours beforehand by the movement. Watches that do not have this device switch over gradually from around 9.00 p.m. to midnight. The technical process for the fast date correction option was also improved—this is essential when a mechanical watch has not been wound for a few days.

Blancpain
Chronograph 2100 Perpetual Calendar, yellow gold, automatic, Blancpain caliber 5585, perpetual calendar, chronograph, from 1999

Baume & Mercier
Calendar Chronograph, rose gold, caliber W72, full calendar, from 1953

Blancpain
Moon Phase Calendar 2100, yellow gold, automatic, Blancpain caliber 1153, full calendar, from 1999

Blancpain
2100 Military Moon Phase Calendar, steel, automatic, Blancpain caliber 1153, full calendar, from 1999

255

Blancpain
Chrono Flyback Perpetual Calendar, steel, automatic, Blancpain caliber 55F8, perpetual calendar, chronograph with Flyback function, from 1999

Blancpain
Le Brassus Equation Marchante, platinum, automatic, Blancpain caliber 3863, perpetual calendar, equation of time indicator, from 2006

Blancpain
Villeret Full Calendar with moon phase, red gold, automatic, Blancpain caliber 6763, from 2006

Blancpain
Le Brassus Grande Complication 1735, platinum, automatic, Blancpain caliber 1735, quarter hour and minute repeater, perpetual calendar, split-second chronograph, from 2006

Martin Braun
Astraios, steel, automatic, ETA caliber 2892-A2 with
Martin Braun module MAB4, annual calendar, sunrise
and sunset indicator, from 2006

Breguet
Perpetual Linear Calendar, yellow
gold, automatic, Breguet caliber
502 QPL, perpetual calendar with
linear arranged indicators,
from 1999

The clockmaking industry performed all kinds
of experiments. In one watch, the date could be
pulled onwards, so to speak, by jerking the
winding crown. Other mechanisms required
swift pressure on the crown. Now, finally, one
method has proved to be the least subject to
problems. Here, the crown can be pulled out
into three positions. Sitting flush against the
watch, the crown functions as a "winder." When
it is fully pulled out, the hands can be adjusted.
Between these two positions on the winding
shaft is a third, and in this one the date ring can
simply be turned onwards until the correct date
is displayed. Today, most watches have this
particular arrangement for setting the date.

The date indicator generally leads a low-key
Cinderella existence, in a small, usually four-
cornered, pierced window in the dial. Often, the
figures in the date indicator are so tiny that they

Breguet
Equation, yellow gold, automatic, Breguet caliber
502 DPE, perpetual calendar with equation of
time indicator, from 1999

Breguet
Perpetual Calendar Power Reserve,
yellow gold, automatic, Breguet
caliber 502 DRP, perpetual calendar
with power reserve, from 1999

Breguet
Perpetual calendar with two spring barrels, yellow gold, automatic, Breguet caliber 591 QPT, perpetual calendar with retrograde date indicator, from 1999

are unreadable and therefore useless, especially for elderly people with failing eyesight. The large date display was an extremely practical innovation, surely not only treasured by people of a "reading glasses" age.

The large date display, now to be found in ever more watches, is not an invention of the 1990s, as one might assume. Individual watches with this kind of indicator were already available in the 1950s. As examples, we can here cite the caliber 211, 216, and 221 of the now defunct Venus movement factory. In these watches, the date was shown by two independently turning disks.

Nowadays several watch companies offer a date indicator with a good-sized legible date. The altered hand movements and calendar mechanisms required are partly new inventions and partly based on earlier designs.

In the advertising for a lady's watch, the Arkade launched in 1994 by A. Lange & Söhne, a small watch movement was at times shown sitting inside a gigantic date ring. The figures on this date ring are about the size of the figures with which the date is shown in the Arkade's dial window. The reader of the advertisement was asked how it was possible to fit this large date indicator into such a small watch, and received the mysterious reply, "Only Lange knows." This sums up the very difficulty that accompanies the increase in size of the date numerals.

The solution is to replace the ring featuring the numbers "1" to "31," which encircles the movement, with two disks (or, as is the case with Lange, one disk and a cross), which are placed directly next to each other or on top of each other and are turned by the hand movement. As only the numbers "0" to "3" and "1" to "9" need to be printed, the digits can be made considerably bigger.

Breguet
Perpetual Calendar, yellow gold, automatic, Breguet caliber 502 QP3, from 1999

Breguet
Chronograph Perpetual Calendar, yellow gold, automatic, Breguet caliber 533 QP, perpetual calendar, from 1999

Breguet
Perpetual Calendar with power reserve, yellow gold, automatic, Breguet caliber 502.3 DRP.1, from 2006

Bulgari

Bulgari Annual Calendar, yellow gold, automatic, Dubois-Dépraz caliber 5733 (base ETA 2892-A2), annual calendar, from 2006

Chopard

Perpetual Calendar, platinum, automatic, base caliber JLC 888, perpetual calendar, from 1999

Carl F. Bucherer

Patravi Tribute to Fritz Brun, red gold, automatic, CFB caliber 1959 (base ETA 2892-A2), perpetual calendar, chronograph, C.O.S.C. certified chronometer, from 2006

Chopard

Chronograph Perpetual Calendar, yellow gold, automatic, base caliber JLC 889/2, perpetual calendar, from 1999

Chopard

L.U.C. Lunar One, red gold, automatic, L.U.C. caliber 1.96 QP, perpetual calendar, C.O.S.C. certified chronometer, from 2006

Chronoswiss
Lunar Full Calendar, yellow gold, automatic, Chronoswiss caliber C.931 (ETA 2892-A2), from 2006

Doxa
Chronograph with full calendar, steel, hand winding, caliber Valjoux 72C, from 1949

De Bethune
Perpetual Calendar with rotating moon phase, white gold, hand winding, DB caliber 2004, moon phase designed as sphere, from 2006

Dubey & Schaldenbrand
Spiral VIP, rose gold, automatic, ETA caliber 7751, full calendar, chronograph, from 2006

Jaquet Droz
Quantième Perpétuel, white gold, automatic, Jaquet Droz caliber 5863, limited edition of 88, from 2006

More than just a date

The weekday indicator is generally moved on by the same mechanism that moves the date, but sometimes by a separate wheel. The indicator mechanism is like that of the date indicator. The weekdays only are inscribed on a thin sheet metal ring equipped with teeth, either once or in varying sequences one after the other. The designers need to take into account that Monday always follows Sunday, no matter whether we are at the end of a month of 30 days or in the February of a leap year. Occasionally there are quick switch arrangements that can be activated by pressing the crown, whereby a light pressure moves the date on, and stronger pressure the weekday indicator. It was of course in the nature of these arrangements that mistakes in switching were often made and therefore the whole month had to be repeated.

Other combinations made no provision for moving the weekday forward (to correct the watch, therefore, it had to be moved on by one week) and the date change was moved forward by pulling the crown. In this last method, the simplest way has once again proved to be the best. Nearly all date and weekday corrections are today done by pulling the winder shaft out to the middle position mentioned above, and then by turning the crown to the left to set the date, and setting the weekday by turning it to the right, or vice versa.

Full and annual calendars

If the display of day and date is not enough for you, choose the full calendar. This term is used for watches that also indicate the month. The month indicator is controlled by the date star, a 31-toothed wheel that makes one rotation every month and then turns the month one step onwards with the month pointer positioned above it. However, as you can deduce from this explanation, the full calendar only recognizes months with 31 days. In months with 30 or

Roger Dubuis
Sympathie bi-retrograde perpetual calendar, rose gold, automatic, RD caliber 5772, date and weekday, with retrograde indicator, from 2006

Dubey & Schaldenbrand
Moondate, rose gold, automatic, ETA caliber 7751, full calendar, chronograph, from 1999

Roger Dubuis
Golden Square Perpetual Calendar, rose gold, automatic, RD caliber 5739, from 2006

Ebel
Perpetual Calendar, yellow gold, automatic, Ebel caliber 136 (base Zenith 400 El Primero), perpetual calendar, chronograph, from 1999

261

Eberhard
Chronograph with full calendar, yellow gold, hand winding, ETA caliber 7761, full calendar, chronograph, from 1999

Eberhard
Replica, sterling silver, hand winding, from 1950

Eberhard
Navymaster, yellow gold, hand winding, ETA caliber 7761, full calendar, chronograph, C.O.S.C. chronometer, from 1999

Louis Erard
1931 Moon Phase, steel, automatic, ETA caliber 2824-2 with full calendar module by Dubois-Dépraz, from 2006

Glashütte Original
1845 Perpetual Calendar, yellow gold, automatic, Glashütte Original caliber 49-01, from 1999

fewer days, the wearer needs to intervene and jump over the non-existent day with an adjustment button, thus moving on to the first of the next month. The next level up is the annual calendar, which only needs correcting in February. Four-year calendars, often also referred to as semi-perpetual calendars, only lose their place every leap year. The wearer only needs to make a correction on February 29.

Watches for your great-grandchildren

The crème de la crème are perpetual calendars, which will give the time, day, date, month, year, or at least leap year, and phase of the moon until March 1, 2100. The year 2100, which probably few of today's proud owners of such complicated watches will live to see, will, as a

Glashütte Original

Karree Perpetual Calendar, yellow gold, automatic, Glashütte Original caliber 42-01, from 1999

Eterna

Calendar watch, yellow gold, hand winding, caliber 1118H, full calendar, from 1945

Girard-Perregaux

Vintage XXL Perpetual Calendar, rose gold, automatic, GP caliber 3170, perpetual calendar, chronograph, from 2006

Glashütte Original

Senator Perpetual Calendar, rose gold, automatic, Glashütte Original caliber 100-02, from 2006

Heuer
Chronograph, full calendar, steel,
hand winding, caliber Valjoux 730,
from 1950

IWC
Novecento, yellow gold, automatic,
IWC caliber C.96061, perpetual calendar
with moon phase indicator, from 1999

IWC
Da Vinci Rattrapante, yellow gold,
automatic, IWC caliber 79251,
perpetual calendar with moon phase
indicator, chronograph with
split-second function, from 1999

IWC
Portuguese Perpetual Calendar, red
gold, automatic, IWC caliber 50611,
double moon phase indicator,
from 2006

IWC
Portofino, platinum, hand winding,
IWC caliber C.18561, perpetual
calendar with moon phase
indicator, from 1999

Jaeger-LeCoultre
Calendar watch, steel/gold-plated, hand winding, JLC caliber 806AW, full calendar, moon phase indicator, from 1945

Jaeger-LeCoultre
Master Moon, steel, automatic, JLC caliber 891/448, full calendar, moon phase indicator, from 1999

IWC
Da Vinci, red gold, automatic, IWC caliber 79261, moon phase indicator, chronograph, from 2006

so-called secular year, not be a leap year. There will therefore be no February 29 in that year. In the Gregorian calendar that we all follow, this is supposed to happen every four years, but with full centuries this only applies if they can be divided by 400. Up until that date, however, the watches on sale today will deliver the expected information—depending, of course, on whether the spring is regularly wound up!

The "perpetual" element has its limits—for example, a slackened spring. If, therefore, an enthusiast for these complex watches wears another timepiece, perhaps for sport or when traveling—which could be a good idea, given the high value of these masterpieces—he or she would have to make sure that the perpetual calendar continues to be supplied with energy. The watch must therefore be wound by hand

Jaeger-LeCoultre
Calendar watch, steel/yellow gold, hand winding, JLC caliber 494/1, full calendar, moon phase indicator, from 1945

Jaeger-LeCoultre

Master Perpetual, red gold, automatic, JLC caliber 889/1-440/1, perpetual calendar, moon phase indicator, from 1999

Jaeger-LeCoultre

Master Eight Days Perpetual, red gold, automatic, JLC caliber 876, perpetual calendar, from 2006

Jaeger-LeCoultre

Master Calendar, red gold, automatic, JLC caliber 924, full calendar, moon phase and power reserve indicator, from 2006

JeanRichard

TV Screen Perpetual Calendar, white gold, automatic, JR caliber 80 33 QJ, perpetual calendar, from 2006

Kelek
Grande Complication, yellow gold, automatic, Kelek caliber 2152-24S, perpetual calendar, chronograph, from 1999

F.P. Journe
Octa Calendar, platinum, automatic, F.P. Journe caliber 1300-2, annual calendar with retrograde date indicator, from 2006

Kelek
52 Calendar Weeks, steel, automatic, Kelek caliber 9252 (base ETA 2892), calendar week indicator, from 1999

Kelek
Semi-perpetual calendar, steel/yellow gold, automatic, Kelek caliber 5700 (base ETA 2892-A2), from 1999

every other day at the least, or permanently turned by a watch mover, so that the automatic oscillating weight tightens the spring. This secures the constant display of all time and calendar information, but has the disadvantage of continuous wear and tear, without allowing you to enjoy this technical wonder. In any case, many of these marvelously complicated watches will probably have to spend their existence in the dark safe of a collector, who wants to own such a watch but would never use it. It's a pity, really.

A short aside—moon phase indicators

The moon, feminine in gender in Latin-based languages and honored in many ancient cultures as a symbol closely connected with fertility, exercises a fascination even over people with no feel for mysticism. At times, the power of the moon is very highly esteemed; for instance, in the case of a hairdresser in Saxony, Germany,

Kurth
Calendar watch, rose gold, automatic, historic Longines caliber with calendar module, from 1999

Maurice Lacroix
Moon phase watch, steel, automatic,
ML caliber 37 (base ETA 2824-2),
full calendar, from 1999

Maurice Lacroix
Masterpiece Phase de Lune Tonneau,
steel, automatic, ML caliber 37
(base ETA 2824-2), full calendar,
from 2006

Maurice Lacroix
Masterpiece Lune Rétrograde, yellow gold, hand
winding, ML caliber 104, (base ETA 6498-2) retrograde
date indicator, 2006

Maurice Lacroix
Masterpiece Calendrier Rétrograde, steel,
hand winding, ML caliber 76 (base ETA 6498-2)
retrograde date indicator, from 2006

A. Lange & Söhne
Langematic Perpetual, yellow gold, automatic,
Lange caliber L922.1 SAX-0-Mat, perpetual
calendar, 24-hour indicator, from 2006

268

who cut her customers' hair at full moon (because certain toxins are supposed to concentrate in the ends of the hairs at that time), and thereby broke the strict German laws on hours of business.

In earlier centuries, astrology generally played a far greater role in people's lives than it does today, and the moon was awarded an importance far in excess of its scientifically proved effects on events on earth (on the tides, for example). The continual changing of the moon from slender crescent to rounded full moon and back to new moon was an early stimulus to clockmakers, heading them towards demonstrating the different forms of our planet's companion, and in particular its regular pattern, by means of a display on a clock.

Longines
Chronograph Moon Phase, yellow gold, hand winding, caliber Valjoux 72C, full calendar, chronograph, from 1979

Longines
Evidenza Moon Phase, steel, automatic, Longines L600 (base ETA 2892-2), full calendar, from 2006

Longines
Master Collection Moon Phase, steel, automatic, Longines caliber L678 (base ETA 7751), full calendar, 24-hour indicator, from 2006

Marcello C.
Full calendar, steel, hand winding, ETA caliber 6497, from 1999

Longines
Conquest Replica Chrono Moon Phase, steel, automatic, Longines caliber L687.2 (base ETA 7751), full calendar, chronograph, 24-hour indicator, from 2006

Mühle Glashütte
Business-Timer, steel, automatic, ETA
caliber 2892-A2 with module built on,
calendar week indicator, from 2006

Minerva
Chronograph with full calendar, steel,
hand winding, caliber Valjoux 723,
from 1955

Franck Muller
Cintrée Curvex Chrono Master Calendar,
rose gold, automatic FM caliber 1870,
full calendar, chronograph, from 1999

Franck Muller
Cintrée Curvex Perpetual Calendar,
yellow gold, automatic, FM caliber RFM93,
perpetual calendar, quarter hour and
minute repeater, from 1999

H. Moser & Cie
Moser-Perpetual 1, red gold, hand
winding, perpetual calendar with
small month indicator cut out of the
center, from 2006

Franck Muller
Rattrapante Q.P. Tourbillon, platinum, automatic,
FM caliber 1790, perpetual calendar, chronograph
with split-second function, from 1999

Franck Muller
Long Island Master Calendar, white gold, automatic, FM 2800, full calendar, from 2006

Nivrel
One year calendar, steel, automatic, ETA caliber 2892-2 with calendar module, from 1999

Franck Muller
Cintrée Curvex Chrono QP Rétrograde, yellow gold, automatic, FM caliber 5888 BR, perpetual calendar with retrograde indicators, chronograph, from 2006

Nivrel
Perpetual calendar 52 weeks, steel, automatic, ETA caliber 2892-2 with calendar module and calendar week indicator, from 1999

Franck Muller
Cintrée Curvex Quantième Perpétuel, white gold, automatic, FM caliber 5888 BR, perpetual calendar with retrograde month indicator, from 2006

271

Omega
Cosmic, red gold, hand winding, caliber 381, full calendar, from 1940

Parmigiani
Toric Quantième Perpetual Rétrograde, white gold, automatic, Parmigiani caliber 333, perpetual calendar with retrograde date indicator, from 2006

Patek Philippe
Perpetual Calendar, white gold, automatic, Patek Philippe caliber 27-4600, perpetual calendar with moon phase display, from 1963

Oris
Complication Tonneau, steel, automatic, Oris caliber 581 (base ETA 2688/2671) 24-hour indicator, from 1999

There are very practical reasons for this, because particularly in the temperate zones of our planet the sky is often cloudy for days on end and the Earth's satellite cannot be seen. What a good thing it is, then, to have a watch that shows the state of affairs above the clouds. Before going to the hairdresser, for instance! It is comparatively simple to represent the phases of the moon within a lunar month (new moon, waxing moon, first quarter, full moon, waning moon, last quarter). The function of the planet Earth, throwing its shadow and for most of the time

allowing only part of the moon to receive sunlight, is shown on a moon phase indicator by correspondingly formed cut-outs in the dial.

Indication of the moon phase is generally via a dark blue disk which is turned under the dial by the movement of the hands. Two large, usually golden dots printed or polished on to the disk opposite one another are shown turn and turn about in the cut-out of the dial. The "moon disk" lying under the watch dial rotates once in 59 days, not quite two months. The reason for

Patek Philippe

Annual calendar, white gold,
automatic, Patek Philippe
caliber 315/198, from 1999

Patek Philippe

Chronograph Perpetual Calendar,
steel, hand winding, Patek Philippe
caliber, perpetual calendar with
moon phase indicator, only two of
these watches were made in steel,
from 1942

Patek Philippe

Chronograph Rattrapante Perpetual
Calendar, yellow gold, automatic,
Patek Philippe caliber 27-70/150,
chronograph with split-second
function, from 1999

Patek Philippe

Gondolo Calendario, white gold,
automatic, Patek Philippe
caliber 324 S QA LU 24H, annual
calendar with moon phase and
24-hour indicators, from 2006

Patek Philippe

Chronograph with perpetual calendar, red gold, automatic, Patek Philippe caliber CH 27-70 Q, perpetual calendar with moon phase indicator, from 2006

Patek Philippe

Perpetual Calendar, yellow gold, automatic, Patek Philippe caliber 240 Q, perpetual calendar with 24-hour indicator, from 2006

Patek Philippe

Sky Moon, white gold, automatic, Patek Philippe caliber 240 LU CL, moon phase, day of lunar month and map of heavens display, from 2006

274

Patek Philippe
Perpetual Calendar, yellow gold,
automatic, Patek Philippe caliber
315/136, perpetual calendar with
retrograde date indicator, from 1999

Paul Picot
Firshire Quantième Perpétuel, rose gold,
automatic, perpetual calendar, from 1999

Daniel Roth
Perpetual Calendar, rose gold, automatic,
Daniel Roth caliber, from 1999

this is the period set in horology as a lunar month (from one new moon to another). This period is a little over 29½ days (29 days, 12 hours, 44 minutes and 2.9 seconds, to be exact). It is known as a synodic month and is the period indicated by most timepieces with a moon phase.

It is easy to work out that this will soon lead to considerable inaccuracies. Two synodic months are not exactly 59 days long, but 59 days, 1 hour, 28 minutes and 5.8 seconds. In high-quality watches, this circumstance is compensated for by specially calculated movements. In the Referenz 5055 by Patek Philippe, for example, the divergence between the moon phase indicator and the actual moon cycle will amount to more than one day only after 122 years and 45 days.

Lange & Söhne have developed a mechanism whereby a round disk under the dial turns in a period of three moon phases, about 88 days and just under 15 hours. This disk shows a section of

Rolex
Perpetual Chronometer Precision, steel,
automatic, from 1950

Robergé
Andromède II, perpetual calendar,
yellow gold, automatic, Dubois-
Dépraz caliber 5100, from 1999

Daniel Roth
Instantaneous Perpetual Calendar, rose gold, automatic, Daniel Roth caliber DR 114, perpetual calendar, from 2006

Daniel Roth
Tourbillon Perpetual Calendar Retro Date, rose gold, automatic, Daniel Roth Caliber DR 740/M070, perpetual calendar with retrograde indicators, from 2006

Daniel Roth
Perpetual Calendar Moon Phases, white gold, automatic, Daniel Roth caliber DR 114, perpetual calendar, from 2006

Schwarz Etienne
Phase de Lune, steel, LIP caliber 3100 (base ETA 2892-2), full calendar with moon phase indicator, from 2006

Daniel Roth
Perpetual Calendar Time Equation, white gold, automatic, Daniel Roth caliber DR 114, perpetual calendar, length of month and time equation indicators, from 2006

Alain Silberstein
Le Perpétuel Anniversaire, steel,
base caliber ETA 2892-A2,
perpetual calendar, from 1999

Sothis
Osiris, steel, ETA caliber 7751,
full calendar with moon phase
indicator, chronograph, from 2006

Sothis
Quantième Spirit of the Moon, steel,
ETA caliber 2824-2 with calendar
module, full calendar with moon
phase indicator, from 1999

Sothis
Chronograph Spirit of the Moon,
steel, ETA caliber 7751, full calendar
with moon phase indicator,
from 1999

Temption
Automat with complication, steel,
Temption caliber T16.2 (base ETA
2892 with calendar module) calendar
week indicator, from 1999

277

its surface in the round window of the dial, and is turned forward by an extensive control movement twice a day, in almost undetectable stages. The display is so accurate that a divergence of one day will appear only after 1058 years. Assuming, of course, that the owner keeps winding the watch up regularly until that point!

Ulysse Nardin
Tellurium Johannes Kepler, platinum, automatic, UN caliber 87, perpetual calendar with astronomic displays, from 1999

Ulysse Nardin
Perpetual Calendar Ludwig, automatic, UN caliber 33, all calendar functions can be adjusted via crown, C.O.S.C. certified chronometer, from 1999

Union
Tradition full calendar, steel, automatic, Union caliber 26-41, from 1999

Union
Johannes Dürrstein 2, rose gold, hand winding, Union caliber 40-02, perpetual calendar, from 2006

Union

Diplomat Perpetual
Calendar, steel, automatic,
Union caliber 26-53,
perpetual calendar,
from 2006

Universal Genève

Calendar watch with moon phase,
white gold, hand winding, caliber
291, full calendar, from 1945

Universal Genève

Tri-Compax, yellow gold, hand
winding, caliber 281, full calendar,
chronograph, from 1948

279

Universal Genève

Complitech, steel, automatic,
Universal Genève caliber 99
(base ETA 7751), perpetual calendar,
chronograph, from 1999

Vacheron Constantin

Chronograph Perpetual Calendar, rose gold,
automatic, VC caliber 1136 QP, perpetual calendar,
chronograph, from 2006

Vacheron Constantin

Calendar watch with moon phase, red gold,
automatic, VC caliber 485, full calendar, from 2006

**Urban Jürgensen &
Sønner**

Referenz 3, platinum, automatic,
perpetual calendar, from 1999

Vacheron Constantine

Malte Perpetual Calendar Retrograde,
platinum, automatic, VC caliber
1126 QPR, perpetual calendar with
retrograde date indicator, from 2006

280

Wakmann
Chronograph with full calendar,
hand winding, caliber Valjoux 730,
from 1975

Vacheron Constantin
Malte Chronograph Perpetual Calendar
Retrograde, yellow gold, automatic,
VC caliber 1126 QPR, perpetual calendar,
chronograph, from 2006

Zenith
Chronomaster Chronograph, yellow
gold, automatic, Zenith caliber 410
El Primero, full calendar, from 1999

George J. von Burg
Perpetual Calendar, rose gold, automatic,
Dubois-Dépraz caliber 2110 (base ETA
2892-A2), perpetual calendar,
chronograph, from 2006

Xemex
Piccadilly Calendario Reserve, rose
gold, automatic, Soprod caliber 9075
(base ETA 2892-A2) calendar week
indicator, from 2006

9. REPEATER WATCHES

If you want to know the time at night, you turn the light on in order to see your watch. It's easy enough, these days. But in the seventeenth century, the situation was quite different. For this reason, ingenious clockmakers devised a striking mechanism for pocket watches that would tell you the time even in darkness. Today, making repeater watches is one of the most difficult challenges a watchmaker can be set. For this reason, they are rare—and the prices paid for them correspondingly high.

Audemars Piguet

Grande Complication, platinum, hand winding, AP caliber 2885, hour, quarter hour, and minute repeater, perpetual calendar, split-second chronometer, from 1999

Audemars Piguet

Triple Complication, yellow gold, hand winding, AP caliber 2880, hour, quarter hour, and minute repeater, perpetual calendar, chronograph, from 1999

Audemars Piguet

Grande Sonnerie, yellow gold, hand winding, AP caliber 2868, hour and quarter hour repetition, grand and small strike repeater movement, chronograph, from 1999

Audemars Piguet

Jules Audemars tourbillon minute repeater, red gold, hand winding, AP caliber 2874, from 2006

The first striking clocks were made very shortly after the first mechanical ones. This addition was introduced on very practical grounds. Clockmakers were simply concerned with broadcasting time information from church towers—in those days, the only places clocks were to be found—even during the long periods of darkness of the European winter. So even during the night, those living in the parish would know at least more or less that "the hour had struck." At first, only full hours struck; later, there were striking movements that marked the half and quarter hours.

Audemars Piguet
Minute Repeater Jump Hour, yellow gold,
hand winding, AP caliber 2865, hour, quarter
hour and minute repeater, digital jump hour
indicator, from 1999

Audemars Piguet
Jules Audemars Dynamographe,
white gold, hand winding, AP caliber
2981, strike movement with three
gongs, from 2006

Blancpain
Le Brassus Grande Complication 1735, platinum,
automatic, Blancpain caliber 1735, quarter hour
and minute repeater, perpetual calendar,
split-second chronograph, from 1999

Blancpain
Minute Repeater 2100, yellow gold,
automatic, Blancpain caliber 35,
quarter hour and minute repeater,
from 1999

Blancpain
Minute repeater, platinum,
automatic, Blancpain caliber 35,
quarter hour and minute repeater,
from 2006

The first striking pocket watches date from the seventeenth century. That horological genius, Abraham Louis Breguet, is given credit for the greatest role in the development of this complication, as he replaced the bells with space-saving gongs.

The practical reason that rang alongside the above-mentioned horological challenge remained the same. Wealthy gentlemen, who in those days were the only people who could afford such watches, were to have the opportunity to tell the time even in the dark. This was the purpose of the so-called repeater clocks and watches, where a sliding bolt or push-button wound up the spring of the strike movement, which then instantly gave the time by sound, and was more or less accurate (according to design).

De Witt
Académia Répétition Minutes, red gold,
hand winding, De Witt caliber, 1188
(base Claret 88), quarter hour and
minute repeater, from 2006

Breguet
Minute repeater, perpetual calendar,
platinum, hand winding, Breguet
caliber 567 RMP, from 2006

Bulgari
Anfiteatro Répétition Minutes,
platinum, hand winding, GP caliber
9950, quarter hour and minute
repeater, from 2006

Corum

Admiral's Cup, quarter hour repeater,
yellow gold, automatic, Corum caliber 58
(base caliber Fréderic Piguet 70), repeater
with movable images in three dial windows,
from 1999

Roger Dubuis

MuchMore minute repeater, white
gold, hand winding, RD caliber 26,
quarter hour and minute repeater,
limited edition of 28, from 2006

Chronoswiss

Répétition à Quarts, steel, automatic,
Chronoswiss caliber C.126 (base Enicar 165
with strike movement module), quarter hour
repeater, from 2006

Epos

Répétition 5 Minutes, steel,
automatic, Dubois-Dépraz caliber
D 88, five minute repeater,
from 2006

287

Girard-Perregaux
Richeville Minute Repeater, yellow gold, hand winding, GP caliber 9896, hour, quarter hour, and minute repeater, perpetual calendar, from 1999

IWC
Il Destriero Scafusia, red gold, hand winding, IWC caliber C.18680, hour, quarter hour, and minute repeater, tourbillon, perpetual calendar, split-second chronograph, from 1999

The strikes varied from hour strike, to hour and quarter hour strike, to timepieces with minute repeaters, where first the hours, then the quarter hours elapsed since the last full hour, and finally the minutes that had passed since the last quarter, were struck. To differentiate the strikes, different tones were created by hammers striking on two gongs, alone or in a duet. The most usual sequence is this: The deep note alone sounds on the hour, the quarter hour is indicated by a simultaneous stroke on both gongs, and only the higher gong is used for the minutes.

Gérald Genta
Grande Sonnerie, white gold, automatic, caliber GG 8561, hour, quarter hour, and minute repeater, grand and lesser strike movement, tourbillon, from 1999

De Grisogono
Occhio, red gold, hand winding, minute repeater with three gongs, dial segment mechanism opens when repeater strike is operated, from 2006

Gérald Genta
Octo Minute Repeater, red gold, automatic, caliber GG 8561, quarter hour and minute repeater, digital jump hour indicator, from 2006

IWC

Grande Complication, platinum, automatic, IWC caliber C.79091, hour, quarter hour, and minute repeater, perpetual calendar, chronograph, from 1999

Kelek

Five minute repeater, yellow gold, automatic, Kelek caliber DK 87 (base ETA caliber with module), from 1999

Kelek

Quarter hour repeater, steel, automatic, Kelek caliber DK 94 (base ETA caliber with module), from 1999

Jaeger-LeCoultre

Minute Repeater Antoine LeCoultre, platinum, hand winding, JLC caliber 947, power reserve and torque indicators, from 2006

290

An even more complicated strike movement, the sonnerie (from the French *sonner*, meaning "to sound," "to ring") has the strikes initiated independently by the watch movement itself. A *petite sonnerie* sounds automatically when the full hour is reached, a *grande sonnerie* every quarter hour. And, of course, the strike can be activated at any time by the repeater bolt. Such a strike movement can be further extended by having extra gongs built in. You can then have a little melody played, such as the chime of "Big Ben." This is known as a *carillon*—translated, that simply means "a ring of bells."

Franck Muller
Cintrée Curvex Tourbillon Repeater, FM caliber TFM 95, hour, quarter hour, and minute repeater, tourbillon, from 1999

Parmigiani
Toric Corrector, platinum, hand winding, Parmigiani caliber 255, minute repeater, perpetual calendar, from 2006

JeanRichard
TV Screen minute repeater, white gold, hand winding, JR caliber 88 (base Claret 88), quarter hour and minute repeater, from 2006

Franck Muller
Conquistador, platinum, automatic, FM caliber RMQPR, hour, quarter hour, and minute repeater, perpetual calendar, from 1999

Nivrel
Five minute repeater, steel, automatic, Dubous-Dépraz caliber 87 (base ETA 2892-A2), from 2006

Parmigiani
Toric Westminster, platinum, hand winding, Parmigiani caliber 252, quarter hour and minute repeater with four gongs (Westminster chimes), 24-hour indicator (second zone time), from 2006

Daniel Roth
Grande Sonnerie, white gold, automatic, caliber DR 760 (base GG 3100), quarter hour and minute repeater with four gongs (Westminster chimes), from 2006

Parmigiani
Kalpa XL Répétition Minutes, platinum, hand winding, Parmigiani caliber 350, quarter hour and minute repeater, from 2006

Robergé
Andromède II Répétition Minutes, white gold, hand winding, base caliber Lémania 2179, from 1999

Paul Picot
Atelier 818 minute repeater, rose gold, hand winding, hour, quarter hour, and minute repeater, from 1999

The miniaturization of the striking movement to wristwatch size is, along with the tourbillon, the crowning pinnacle of the watchmaker's art. Here, we can give only a brief indication of the complex way in which a small timepiece striking mechanism functions. The number of strikes is determined by notched cams, so-called "snails," constantly rotated by the movement of the watch. Curved, toothed racks are forced by the pressure of small springs to drop into the notches—at different heights, according to the time—and are then transported, tooth by tooth, to their rest position by a train. The number of revolutions required in this process determines how often the hammer strikes the gong, which is wound around the watch movement.

Daniel Roth
Minute repeater and perpetual calendar, white gold, hand winding, Daniel Roth caliber, hour, quarter hour, and minute repeater, from 1995

Daniel Roth
Elipsocurvex Minute Repeater, white gold, automatic, caliber DR 750, minute repeater, from 2006

Urban Jürgensen & Sønner
Minute repeater, platinum, hand winding, hour, quarter hour, and minute repeater, from 2006

293

Ulysse Nardin
San Marco Sonnerie en passant, platinum, automatic, UN caliber 75, hour and half hour repeater en passant or on request, figure on the dial moves during course of repeater chime, from 1999

The chime is initiated, as mentioned above, by a sliding bolt. This is usually situated on the left side of the case. If it is pulled downwards, the wearer thus provides energy to the strike movement, and when it is released the chime is heard as described above. If the bolt is not moved energetically enough, the watch will sound the wrong time. For this reason, good strike movements have the so-called "all or nothing" switch: If the repeater mechanism is activated wrongly or not firmly enough, nothing happens. However, if the watch chimes, the wearer can be sure that the number of rings corresponds to the time indicated on the dial.

Harry Winston
Perpetual Calendar with minute repeater, platinum, hand winding, from 1999

Vacheron Constantin
Les Complications minute repeater, yellow gold, hand winding, Vacheron Constantin caliber 1755 QP, hour, quarter hour, and minute repeater, perpetual calendar, from 1999

Vacheron Constantin
Les Complications minute repeater skeleton, yellow gold, Vacheron Constantin caliber 1755 QP, hour, quarter hour, and minute repeater, from 1999

Vacheron Constantin

Tour de l'Ile, rose gold, hand winding, Vacheron Constantin caliber
2750, 16 complications including minute tourbillon, minute
repeater, perpetual calendar, and equation of time indicator,
jubilee edition to celebrate 250th anniversary of the company,
limited edition of seven, from 2005

10. INDEX

INDEX

Muller, Franck, Cintrée Curvex Chrono Master Calendar 270

Muller, Franck, Cintrée Curvex Chrono QP Rétrograde 271

Muller, Franck, Cintrée Curvex Jumping Hour 54

Muller, Franck, Cintrée Curvex Perpetual Calendar 270

Muller, Franck, Cintrée Curvex Quantième Perpétuel 271

Muller, Franck, Cintrée Curvex Seconde Rétrograde 53

Muller, Franck, Cintrée Curvex Tourbillon Imperiale 247

Muller, Franck, Cintrée Curvex Tourbillon Repeater 291

Muller, Franck, Cintrée Curvex World Time 214

Muller, Franck, Conquistador 291

Muller, Franck, Conquistador Chronograph 111

Muller, Franck, Long Island 54

Muller, Franck, Long Island Master Calendar 271

Muller, Franck, Long Island Tourbillon 247

Muller, Franck, Master Banker 215

Muller, Franck, Master City 111

Muller, Franck, Master Formula 215

Muller, Franck, Rattrapante Q.P. Tourbillon 270

N

N.B. Yaeger, Charlie 160

N.B. Yaeger, Delta 160

N.B. Yaeger, Tango 160

Nienaber, King Size RetroLator 54

Nivada, Aviator Sea Diver 159

Nivada, Depthomatic 180

Nivrel, Alarm 232

Nivrel, Automatic Day Date 159

Nivrel, Chronograph Large Minute Hand 112

Nivrel, Five Minute Repeater 291

Nivrel, One Year Calendar 271

Nivrel, Perpetual Calendar 52 Weeks 271

Nomos, Orion 55

Nomos, Tangente 55

Nomos, Tangente Date Power Reserve 55

Nomos, Tetra 55

Nouvelle Horologie Calabrese, Analogica 54

O

Officine Panerai, Luminor Marina 57

Officine Panerai, Luminor Submersible 57

Omega, Aviator Watch 160

Omega, Aviator Watch Air Ministry 160

Omega, Chronograph, 1938 112

Omega, Chronograph, 1939 112

Omega, Cosmic 272

Omega, De Ville Co-Axial Chronograph Rattrapante 112

Omega, De Ville Tonneau 56

Omega, Dynamic Chrono 114

Omega, Flightmaster 161

Omega, Men's Watch 56

Omega, Seamaster 300 181

Omega, Seamaster Automatic 600 m Ploprof 181

Omega, Seamaster Automatic Chronometer 56

Omega, Seamaster Chrono Diver 300 m 181

Omega, Seamaster GMT 215

Omega, Seamaster Memomatic 232

Omega, Seamaster Omegamatic 56

Omega, Seamaster Planet Ocean Co-Axial 181

Omega, Seamaster Professional Chrono Diver 112

Omega, Seamaster Professional Diver 181

Omega, Seamaster Railmaster XXL Chronometer 54

Omega, Seamaster XVI 55

Omega, Speedmaster Broad Arrow 112

Omega, Speedmaster Day-Date 113

Omega, Speedmaster Moonwatch Replica 161

Omega, Speedmaster Professional, 1999 113

Omega, Speedmaster Professional, 1963 160

Omega, Speedmaster Professional Mk II 112

Oris, Atelier Complication 216

Oris, Big Crown Chronograph 114

Oris, Big Crown Complication 216

Oris, Big Crown Pointer Date 57

Oris, Complication Tonneau 272

Oris, Flight Timer 161

Oris, Rectangular Classic 56

Oris, TT1 Divers Titanium 182

Oris, TT1 Divers Titanium Chronograph 182

Oris, TT1 Divers Titanium Date 182

Oris, TT1 Master Diver 182

Oris, Williams F1 Chronograph 114

Oris, Worldtimer 216

P

Panerai, Luminor 1950 Rattrapante 114

Panerai, Luminor Egittica 183

Panerai, Luminor Submersible 2500 183

Panerai, Radiomir Base 57

Panerai, Radiomir Brevattato 183

Parmigiani, Bugatti 370 Type 58

Parmigiani, Kalpa XL Hebdomadaire 57

Parmigiani, Kalpa XL Répétition Minutes 292

Parmigiani, Kalpa XL Tourbillon 248

Parmigiani, Toric Corrector 291

Parmigiani, Toric Quantième Perpetual Rétrograde 272

Parmigiani, Toric Répétition Minutes GMT 216

Parmigiani, Toric Westminster 292

Patek Philippe, 10 Jours Tourbillon 248

Patek Philippe, Annual Calendar 273

Patek Philippe, Aquanaut 60

Patek Philippe, Asymmétrique 59

Patek Philippe, Calatrava, 1953 58

Patek Philippe, Calatrava, 1999 60

Patek Philippe, Calatrava Grande Taille 60

Patek Philippe, Calatrava Travel Time 217

Patek Philippe, Chronograph Perpetual Calendar 274

Patek Philippe, Chronograph Perpetual Calendar, 1942 273

Patek Philippe, Chronograph with Perpetual Calendar, 2006 274

Patek Philippe, Chronograph Rattrapante Perpetual Calendar 273

Patek Philippe, Chronograph Waterproof 115

Patek Philippe, Men's Watch, 1932 58

Patek Philippe, Men's Watch, 1976 59

Patek Philippe, Men's Watch, Art Déco 58

Patek Philippe, Men's Watch for Gübelin 59

Patek Philippe, Gondolo 1999 60

Patek Philippe, Gondolo, 2006 61

Patek Philippe, Gondolo Calendario 273

Patek Philippe, Moon Phase 59

Patek Philippe, Nautilus, 1999 61

Patek Philippe, Nautilus, 2006 61

Patek Philippe, Neptune 60

Patek Philippe, Perpetual Calendar, 1963 272

Patek Philippe, Perpetual Calendar, 1999 275

Patek Philippe, Perpetual Calendar, 2006 274

Patek Philippe, Sky Moon 274

Patek Philippe, Travel Time 217

Patek Philippe, World Time Watch 217

Paul Gerber, Model 33 Moon Phase 39

Paul Gerber, Retro Twin 39

Péquignet, Mooréa Chronograph 115

Péquignet, Mooréa Chronograph Tonneau 115

Péquignet, Mooréa Power Reserve 58

Péquignet, Mooréa Réveil 232

Perrelet, Air Zermatt II 161

Perrelet, Dipteros/Temptest 59

Philippe Charriol, Celtic Le Tourbillon 242

Philippe Charriol, Supersports Chronograph 87

Piaget, Altiplano ultrathin 62

Piaget, Emperador retrograde second 62

Piaget, Légende Rectangle à l'Ancienne 61

Piaget, Polo 62

Piaget, Tradition 61

Picot, Paul, Atelier 1100 Régulateur 62

Picot, Paul, Atelier 818 Minute Repeater 292

Picot, Paul, Atelier Split-Second Chronograph 115

Picot, Paul, Firshire 1937 62

Picot, Paul, Firshire Quantième Perpétuel 275

Picot, Paul, Firshire Tonneau 3000 Retrograde 63

Picot, Paul, Firshire Tonneau Chronograph 115

Picot, Paul, Gentleman Chrono GMT 217

Picot, Paul, Le Chronograph Mythique 116

Picot, Paul, Le Plongeur C-Type Chronograph 184

Picot, Paul, Le Plongeur C-Type Date 184

Picot, Paul, Technograph 116

Pierce, Alarm 233

Poljot, JAK-7 161

Poljot, Red October 184

Porsche Design, Indicator 117

Porsche Design, P 6612 PAC 116

Porsche Design, P 6613 PGR 116

R

Rado, Anatom 63

Rado, Original 63

Rado, Original Diver 185

Rado, Sintra XXL 63

Record, Aviator Watch 162